PRANIC
PSYCHOTHERAPY

PRANIC PSYCHOTHERAPY

Choa Kok Sui

SAMUEL WEISER, INC.

York Beach, Maine

If an ailment is severe or if symptoms are persistent, please consult a physician immediately, preferably one with a holistic medical approach. The material in this book is not intended to replace competent medical treatment.

First published in 1993 by
Samuel Weiser, Inc.
Box 612
York Beach, Maine 03910-0612

02 01 00 99 98 97 96
10 9 8 7 6 5 4 3 2

This work was first published under the auspices of the Institute for Inner Studies, Inc., 855 Pasay Road, corner of Amorsolo Street, Makati 1200, Metro Manila, Philippines.

Library of Congress Cataloging-in-Publication Data
Choa Kok Sui
Pranic psychotherapy / by Choa Kok Sui.
p. cm.
Includes bibliographical references and index.
1. Mind and body therapies. 2. Vital force. 3. Yoga, Hatha.
I. Title.
RC489.M53S85 1993
615.8'51—dc20 92-45544
CIP

ISBN 0-87728-783-X
EB

Typeset in 11 pt Galliard

Printed in the United States of America

The paper used in this publication meets the minimum requirements of the American National Standard for Permanence of Paper for Printed Library Materials Z39.48-1984.

Dedicated
to the nuns and others who are the embodiment
of divine compassion and mercy, and who have worked unceasingly
for the poor and the sick.

Contents

Foreword

There are countless realities completely unknown to us. There are countless ways that only a few have tried, and countless roads that have remained untrodden. This book is one of them. It seeks to make known what has been hidden and offers an invitation—a challenge—to go beyond the confines of set beliefs, practices, and training in order to pursue a quest for wholeness and integration.

Non-believers or skeptics cannot pass judgment on the merits of pranic psychotherapy without first having a taste of it. As it is both a science and an art, experimentation, validation, and practice are essential. The book may well serve its purpose if we keep an open mind to the basic concepts of this healing method as it makes use of both physical and metaphysical methods of healing in relation to the human energy field and aura. The material presented here even provides a new dimension to the field of psychotherapy.

My first encounter with pranic healing occurred when I was becoming dissatisfied with the rate of healing my patients experienced through the use of current trends in psychiatric treatment. I got a copy of the author's first book, *Pranic Healing,* and from there developed an interest in the field of pranic psychotherapy. I took the basic and advanced courses and have practiced the method that this book now aims to present.

There are areas of similarities and differences which exist in the psychodynamics of pranic psychotherapy and conventional psychiatric treatment. I discovered that one aspect of pranic psychotherapy which can be closely related to psychiatry is in the specific field of psychological factors affecting a physical condition–psychosomatic medicine. This refers to how the mind, emotions, and life experiences affect the constitution. Examples of these are peptic ulcers, ulcerative colitis, cardiovascular diseases, respiratory disorders–like asthma–skin problems, bone diseases and rheumatoid arthritis, among others. Negative thoughts and feelings apparently have adverse effects on the body.

However, in neurotic cases, the symptoms are the same, but the causes of the illness are different. Pranic theories on psychosis totally differ from that of the classic and current trends in psychiatry. Yet in spite of their differences, this pranic method of psychotherapy can be applied to almost all cases of mental disorder.

I learned that the combination of pranic psychotherapy and conventional psychiatric treatment helped patients considerably and many cases I treated have been used as testimonials in the book. Many of these people experienced immediate relief of symptoms during the first session, whereas others felt better or relieved a day or two after pranic healing. The following cases are examples.

> Morris complained of severe exhaustion, depression, and intense anger caused primarily by his disappointment because a member of the family left him feeling betrayed. After only one healing session, he immediately felt relieved as if something was taken off his chest. Physically, he regained his strength, feeling the surge of renewed energy, and feeling emotionally recharged.
>
> Another case is that of a business executive–a middle manager in a highly competitive business–who consulted with me because he was suffering from insomnia, migraine headaches, heaviness on the chest, and severe phys-

> ical exhaustion. It was discovered that the reasons for these symptoms were the pressures and demands of a job that weighed heavily on his shoulders. When I scanned the patient, I found that his solar plexus and navel chakras were congested. After applying pranic psychotherapy, the patient felt relieved and exclaimed, "Gumaan ang pakiramdam ko" (feel light).

Pranic breathing, the Meditation on Twin Hearts, and creative visualization can be taught to patients easily. The techniques are simple, but effective. The active participation of patients using these methods, coupled with their knowledge of the psychodynamics of aural scanning, enhances fast recovery.

Besides the very interesting chapters on the healing of stress, anxiety, addiction, and other disorders, the section on health problems encountered by psychotherapists is clearly explained and even provides ways to prevent the ill effects of such hazards.

Another feature discussed in this book is healing by prayer. The spiritual and religious dimension of healing is one aspect that can be developed by those who wish to broaden their horizons in their profession or ministry.

Pranic psychotherapy is a good subject for psychological research. I would like to take this opportunity to invite our colleges of medicine and fellow psychiatrists to test for themselves the benefits of this ancient science and art of healing. It would certainly be a great contribution to the medical world and would be a tremendous help to those afflicted with these illnesses.

Dr. Sonia L. Dy, Psychiatrist
Metropolitan Hospital
Sta. Cruz, Metro Manila

Acknowledgments

To my Respected Teachers, especially Respected Teacher Mei Ling, and others for their time and help.

Introduction

There are more things in Heaven and Earth, Horatio, than are dreamt of in your philosophy.

–Shakespeare
Hamlet I.V 166.

This book is a sequel to *Pranic Healing*. The first book deals with the use of pranic healing on physical ailments while this second book deals with psychological ailments. Pranic psychotherapy is simply pranic healing applied to prevent, alleviate and treat psychological ailments. In spite of tremendous progress made in the field of science and medicine, treatments for ailments such as depression, alcoholism, drug addiction, and the like are expensive, difficult and take a long time to perform.

It is the aim of pranic psychotherapy to complement modern medicine and help alleviate the suffering of millions of patients suffering from psychological ailments by using esoteric principles and techniques that have been used for thousands of years.

One of the most common psychological ailments is stress at work or at home. It is also one of the major contributing factors in the breakdown of a marriage. It is the aim of pranic psychotherapy to save and improve relationships in the family by effectively healing stress.

Some of the principles that we will discuss will be "new and quite strange" for many readers. Readers are expected to maintain an open but discriminating mind. Intelligent readers should not be closed-minded nor gullible but should study this book with a clear and objective mind. The ultimate criterion is whether the healing techniques presented really work. The test of the pudding is in eating, not in empty talk and speculations.

To effectively use the healing techniques presented, it is required that readers be proficient in intermediate pranic healing. And those without a pranic healing background have to practice elementary and intermediate pranic healing for several months. They may experiment treating simple psychological ailments like stress, irritability, grief, phobia, and light depression. Severe ailments will require an experienced and proficient pranic healer.

C.K.S.

Basic Concepts, Principles, and Techniques

And his fame went throughout all Syria: and they brought unto him all sick people that were taken with divers diseases and torments, and those which were possessed with devils, and those which were lunatick, and those that had the palsy; and he healed them.[1]

–Matthew 4:24

Most scientists assume that life can exist only in a physical life form. They send spaceships to other planets, looking for signs of physical life, not considering that life "may" also exist in energy or an etheric form. Based on clairvoyant investigation, life exists in an etheric (energy) form and there are etheric beings of different degrees of awareness and development.

–C.K.S.

IN ORDER TO comprehend pranic psychotherapy, it is necessary to understand the following basic esoteric concepts and principles:

---

1 *The New English Bible: with the Apocrypha* (New York: Oxford University Press, 1971). All biblical references in this book come from this version of the Bible.

A) chakras (or major energy centers) and their psychological functions;

B) traumatic psychic energy and thought entities;

C) the chakra and its protective web;

D) negative etheric elementals or etheric parasites.

THE CHAKRAS AND THEIR PSYCHOLOGICAL FUNCTIONS

The major chakras (or energy centers) control and energize the internal organs and also control and affect one's psychological conditions. In other words, they are centers for certain psychological functions. See figure 1 for an illustration of the chakras. In order to make sure that readers understand how we will work with chakras, I present the following discussion.

1) **Basic chakra.** This energy center is located at the base of the spine. The basic chakra is the center of self-preservation or instinct of survival. People who are depressed or suicidal have depleted and underactivated basic chakras. People who have lost touch with physical reality, or who have become quite unrealistic, also have depleted basic chakras. People who, in spite of their qualifications and relatively good health, have difficulty getting jobs have partly depleted or underactivated basic chakras.

2) **Sex chakra.** This energy center is located in the pubic area. It is the center of the sexual instinct. People with strong sex chakras usually have strong sex drives.

3) **Navel chakra.** This energy center is located on the navel. It is the center of the "instinct of knowing."

4) **Meng Mein chakra.** This energy center is located at the back of the navel. It has something to do with the upward flow of pranic energy from the basic chakra. Patients who are violent

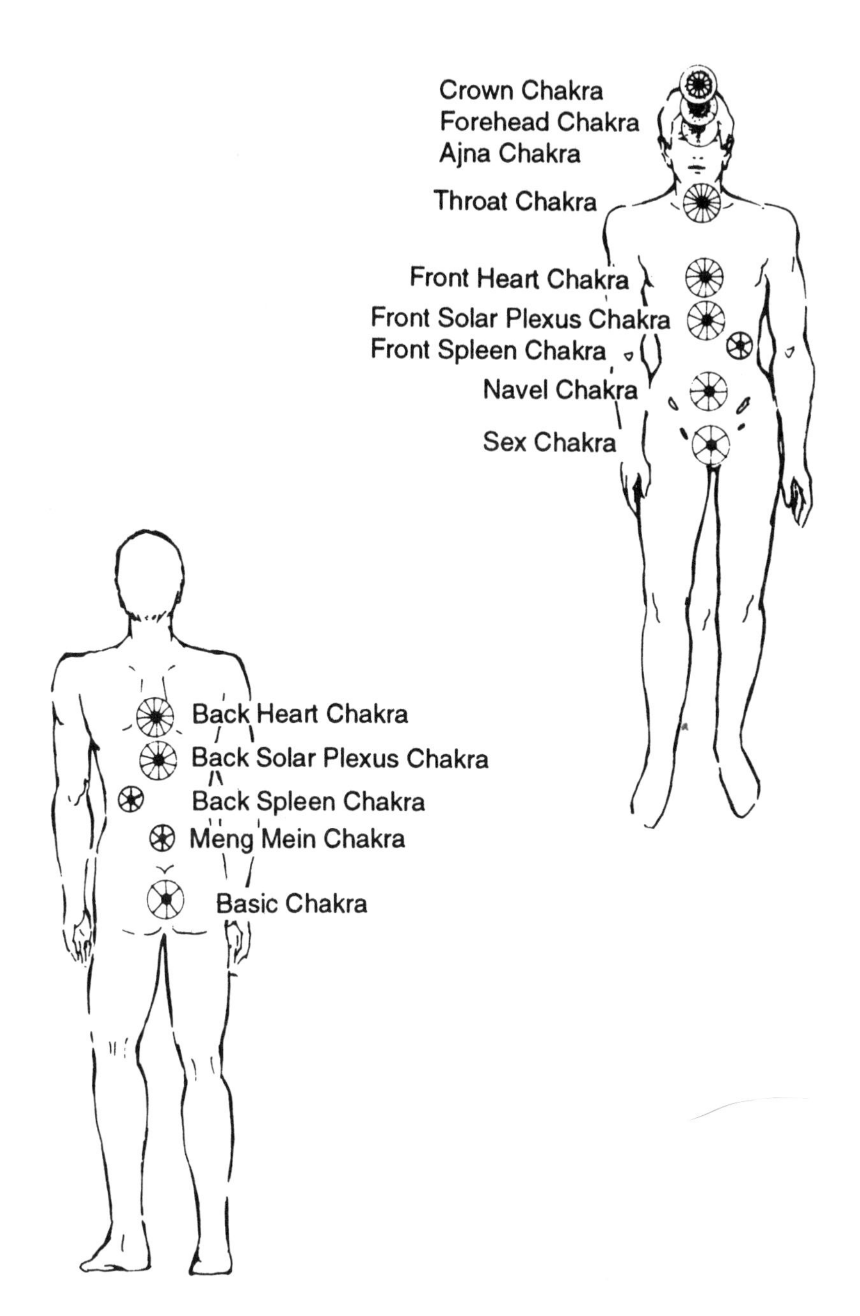

Figure 1. The eleven chakras.

have overactivated meng mein chakras. This energy center should only be handled by experienced or advanced pranic healers. In infants, this chakra should not be energized because of possible harmful effects. With children, older patients, and pregnant women, it is also not advisable to energize this chakra because of possible negative reactions. It is better to avoid unnecessary risks. For more information about the meng mein chakra, read the master healing technique explained in *Pranic Healing*.

5) **Spleen chakra.** The front spleen chakra is located on the center of the left lowermost front rib. In other words, it is located just below the left breast. The back spleen chakra is located at the back of the front spleen chakra. People who are depressed have depleted spleen chakras.

6) **Solar plexus chakra.** The front solar plexus is located at the hollow area between the front ribs. The back solar plexus is located at the back of the front solar plexus chakra. The solar plexus chakra is the center of lower emotions, such as anger, hate, irritation, resentment, worry, anxiety, tension, fear, selfishness, aggressiveness, abrasiveness, addiction, and the like. When people are physically violent, the ajna, solar plexus, basic, and meng mein chakras become overactivated. But the main chakra that influences the other chakras is the solar plexus chakra. By normalizing (through cleansing and energizing) this chakra, violent people can be calmed down in a short period. In healing psychological ailments, this chakra is almost always treated. It is also the center of courage, daring, perseverance, and the desire to win.

7) **Heart chakra.** The front heart chakra is located in front of the heart or at the center of the chest. The back heart chakra is located at the back of the heart. The heart chakra is the center of higher emotions such as peace, serenity, joy, compassion, kindness, gentleness, tenderness, caring, considerateness, patience, and sensitivity. By activating the heart chakra, the lower emotional energies can be transmuted into higher forms of emotional energies. This is why psychologically ill patients must do the Meditation on Twin Hearts twice a day for several months. It will

be better if they can do it daily for the rest of their lives. In acupuncture, hysterical people can be calmed down by stimulating certain acupuncture points which also activate the heart chakra.

8) **Throat chakra.** This is located at the center of the throat. It is the center of the lower mental faculty–the concrete mind. It is used when meticulous details are involved, like studying, planning, painting, and the like. It is also the center of higher creativity while the sex chakra is the center of "physical creativity" or procreation. When the throat chakra is quite strong and active, the sex chakra is also quite active. This is why creative artists also have strong sexual drives.

9) **Ajna chakra.** This is located between the eyebrows. It is the center of higher mental faculty–the abstract mind–and is also the "directing center" or the "will" center.

10) **Forehead chakra.** This chakra controls the nervous system and is the center of lower buddhic or cosmic consciousness.

11) **Crown chakra.** This chakra is located at the crown (or top) of the head. It controls the brain and is the center of higher buddhic faculty or higher cosmic consciousness. The buddhic faculty (when fully developed) manifests as "direct knowing or perception." It is knowing without needing to study. What is learned through the buddhic faculty in a few minutes will require weeks, if not months, to put into words. One with only a developed mental faculty will have to plow or muddle through a problem, whereas another with even only a partly developed buddhic faculty has a quick overall grasp of the problem and the possible solutions. The mental faculty is then used to check on the validity of the solution and to "materialize" that solution. Unfortunately, our present educational system does not encourage the development of the buddhic faculty on the grounds that it provides answers that are not materialistic in nature.

Mental faculty can be compared to a blind man, while the buddhic faculty can be compared to a person who can see. In order for a blind man to have an idea of the shape of an elephant, he has to spend considerable time touching the elephant and trying to deduce and synthesize the data gathered, while one who can see will immediately know that shape. Buddhic consciousness is understanding the subject matter—not after a long period of study nor through inductive or deductive reasoning, but through immediate and direct comprehension or perception.

TRAUMATIC PSYCHIC ENERGY AND THOUGHT ENTITIES

In esoteric sciences, the mental and emotional energies produced by thinking and feeling have consciousness. What you experience, think, and feel produces psychic beings that are called *thought forms* or *thought entities*. In other words, your thoughts and feelings are real and can affect (or influence) you and other people. If you have had a traumatic experience, the traumatic psychic energies produced are lodged in several chakras (or energy centers) which may manifest as stress or phobia. These traumatic energies have certain degrees of consciousness and are called *traumatic thought entities*. A phobia is nothing more than traumatic fear energy or "fear" thought entities that lodge in a certain chakra. Once the phobia thought entity or the fear energy are partly or completely removed from the chakras by the pranic healer, the patient will feel definite improvement.

A traumatic experience may produce repeated thoughts of fear, poor self-esteem, insecurity, futility, and/or indifference. In the long run, this negative thinking and feeling will produce negative thought entities that have a strong inhibiting effect, manifesting as severe depression.

CHAKRAS, PROTECTIVE WEBS NEGATIVE ELEMENTALS

Located at the back of the chakra near the surface of the body is an "energy web." It is slightly smaller than the chakra by about an inch in diameter. This energy web is called *etheric web* or *protective web* because it acts as a filter to protect the person from negative external influences. See figure 2. If the psychological ailment is not very severe, then some of the protective webs are just cracked. But in more serious cases, some of the protective webs are punctured and have big holes. This makes the patient susceptible to "psychic disturbances" or "intrusions" by negative psychic entities or elementals. In Christian terms, these are called bad spirits. The author prefers not to use the word demon because it is rather harsh and does not give an accurate picture of, or impression on, the nature of the problem. In the Holy Bible, there are many cases of patients with severe psychological ailments who were healed by exorcism or removing the negative elementals. See figure 3 on page 8.

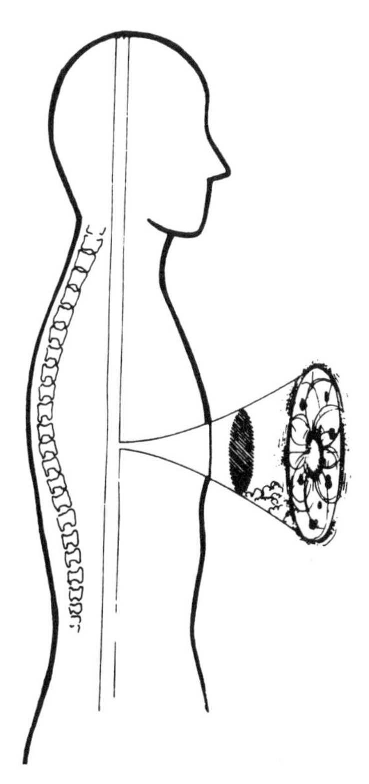

Figure 2. A protective web and chakra filled with negative psychic energies.

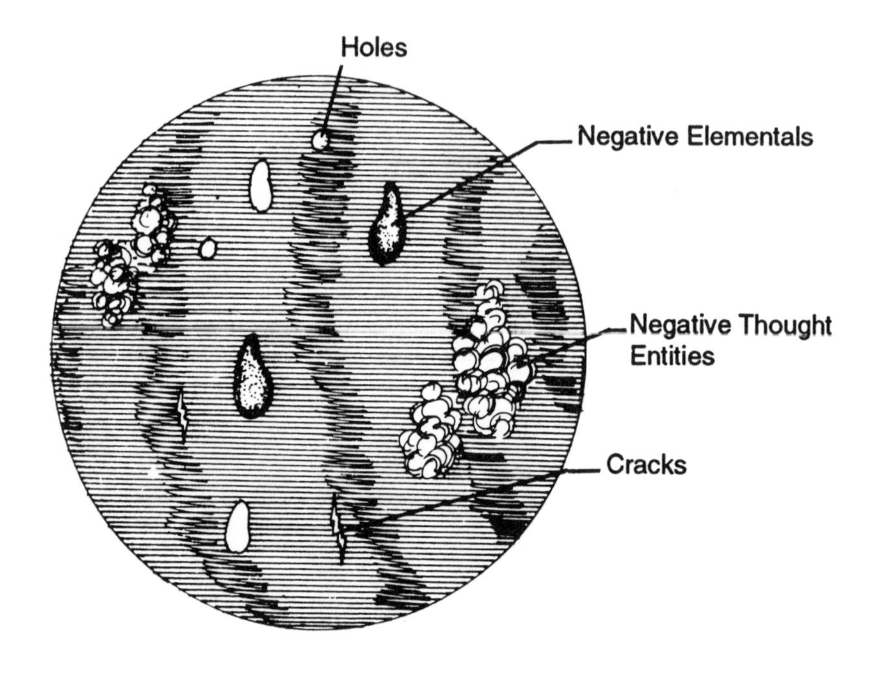

Figure 3. A protective web with holes, cracks, negative thought entities, and negative elementals. Although the thought entities lodged within the chakra and the protective web look like very small gray or dark-colored clouds, they contain a lot of negative psychic energy. This negative psychic energy may be in the form of phobia, obsession, trauma, depression, violence, fear, compulsion, and so on. When a psychic or a clairvoyant focuses attention on negative entities, he or she will intensely experience—emotionally and mentally—the contents of these negative thought forms. Students should keep in mind that negative thought forms or entities are nothing else but repressed traumas or accumulated negative thoughts and feelings. Negative elementals are negative psychic entities which influence a person to behave abnormally.

These negative elementals range from one-third of an inch to several inches in size, depending upon their nature and their degree of influence over the person. They are able to influence a person through cracks or holes in the protective web. Although these negative elementals cause a lot of problems and disturbances in the psychologically imbalanced patient, they are actually quite weak and can easily be destroyed by experienced pranic healers. These negative elementals are nothing more than etheric cockroaches or parasites. They can easily be destroyed by an act of the will of the healer, the use of violet pranic energy, or you can throw them into a water and salt solution.

The difference between a clairvoyant and a "crazy" person is that in a clairvoyant, the etheric or protective web is quite thin and can easily be opened when the clairvoyant faculty is being used. It can also be closed when it is not being used. In other words, the etheric web is just like a shutter that can be opened or closed at will by the clairvoyant. He or she has substantial mastery over the emotions–especially fear–and can see angels, fairies, and negative elementals without becoming psychologically imbalanced. A crazy person, on the other hand, has punctured protective webs and cannot close the holes. He or she is constantly influenced, bothered, or tormented by negative thought entities, negative elementals, and negative disincarnate persons. He or she sees ugly things or hears ugly voices on a regular basis.

Cracks or holes in the protective web are caused by negative thinking, feeling, or habits. Hallucinogenic chemicals burn up part of the protective web. When a person with no spiritual training uses hallucinogenic substances or chemicals, he or she is likely to have quite an unpleasant experience.

When a person is intensely angry, the protective webs of the solar plexus chakra, the ajna chakra, and sometimes also the crown chakra are ruptured. Intense anger attracts negative elementals of a very violent nature. They attach themselves to the angry person through the ruptured protective webs. The angry person then becomes temporarily "possessed" or "insane" and does terrible things that he or she normally would not do. How long these negative elementals will remain attached to a person depends on the character. If he or she is the type that gets intensely angry quite often, then the "insanity" is relatively permanent. These negative elementals feed on anger or need angry energy to survive and, therefore, will regularly incite or stimulate the person to anger.

BASIC TECHNIQUES IN PRANIC HEALING

In elementary and intermediate pranic healing, there are seven basic healing techniques:

1) Sensitizing the hands;

2) Scanning the inner aura;

3) Sweeping (cleansing): general and localized;

4) Increasing the receptivity of the patient;

5) Energizing with prana;

6) Stabilizing the projected pranic energy;

7) Releasing the projected pranic energy or detaching.

In pranic psychotherapy, there are four additional healing techniques:

1) Removing and disintegrating traumatic psychic energy, negative thought entities, negative psychic entities, and negative elementals. This is an advanced cleansing technique.

2) Disintegrating negative elementals and sealing the cracks or holes in the etheric or protective webs. This is an advanced form of energizing.

3) Activating and inhibiting the chakras. This is also an advanced form of energizing.

4) Creating a positive image of the patient or a positive thought entity for the patient.

RELEASING THE PROJECTED PRANIC ENERGY

When healing, the healer should be calm and detached. He or she should not be nervous, "overconcerned," or attached to the expected results. Otherwise, the projected pranic energy will not be released and will return to the healer. The healer needs to be calm and detached in order to release the projected pranic energy. This can be facilitated by visualizing the energy cord between the healer and the patient being cut. A good healer is meticulous and thorough, but, at the same time, calm and detached, while not being indifferent toward the patient.

REMOVING NEGATIVE THOUGHT ENTITIES AND NEGATIVE ELEMENTALS

How will you remove negative thought entities and negative elementals lodged in the different chakras? Imagine that you are a clairvoyant and that a patient with a psychological ailment is in front of you. You are now looking at the dirty negative thought entities and elementals. Instinctively, what will you do? You will reach out to this patient and try to sweep or pluck out the grayish thought entities and negative elementals, just as you would pick up or sweep up pieces of paper or dirt lying on the floor. You notice that the negative thought entities and negative elementals tend to resist. So you exert greater willpower to remove them. The exertion of your willpower is done by just having a clear and steady intent to remove the negative thought entities. You observe that a few come off but a substantial number still remain. So you apply more sweeping until the chakra is completely clean. This is exactly what the healer does, and probably how paranormal or pranic healing was developed. See figure 4 on page 12.

Figure 4. Advanced localized sweeping technique.

If elementary sweeping is applied, this may require as many as fifty sweepings or more in order to thoroughly clean the chakra and its protective web, depending upon the skill of the healer and the severity of the ailment. It is necessary to have a basin of water containing salt to properly dispose of the negative elementals and the thought entities, as we discussed in the first volume.[2]

---

[2] See *Pranic Healing* (York Beach, ME: Samuel Weiser, 1989). You will find complete instructions here for disposing of negative energy.

A more advanced technique that can be used to remove these negative entities is violet pranic energy or violet light. Negative elementals and thought entities are easily overwhelmed and destroyed by violet pranic energy. In other words, violet pranic energy is anti-negative-elementals and anti-negative-thought-entities. When violet pranic energy is used, the number of sweepings required is greatly reduced.

Sweeping has to be done slowly and gently–not too abruptly or willfully–because the chakra and its protective web can be damaged, which may adversely affect the patient's health.

SEALING CRACKS OR HOLES IN THE PROTECTIVE WEB

Cracks or holes in the protective web can easily be sealed by energizing with pranic energy. Elementary or intermediate energizing produces a seal that is not very durable or strong. A more advanced technique creates a seal using violet pranic energy which is more durable and can easily disintegrate negative elementals and thought entities. The use of violet pranic energy reduces energizing time. The effect is stronger and more lasting than just using ordinary white pranic energy. Hence, it requires fewer and less frequent pranic treatments. The seal is stronger and more durable, compared to ordinary white pranic energy and cannot be easily repenetrated by negative elementals. See figure 5 on page 14.

Flicking your hand has to be done frequently when energizing in order to efficiently eliminate dirty energy. *By energizing the affected chakra and the protective web, the cracks or punctures on the protective web are sealed.* But there will be a relapse if the psychological ailment is long-standing; therefore, pranic treatments have to be repeated several times per week until the condition stabilizes. If the ailment is very severe, the treatments have to be repeated several times a day.

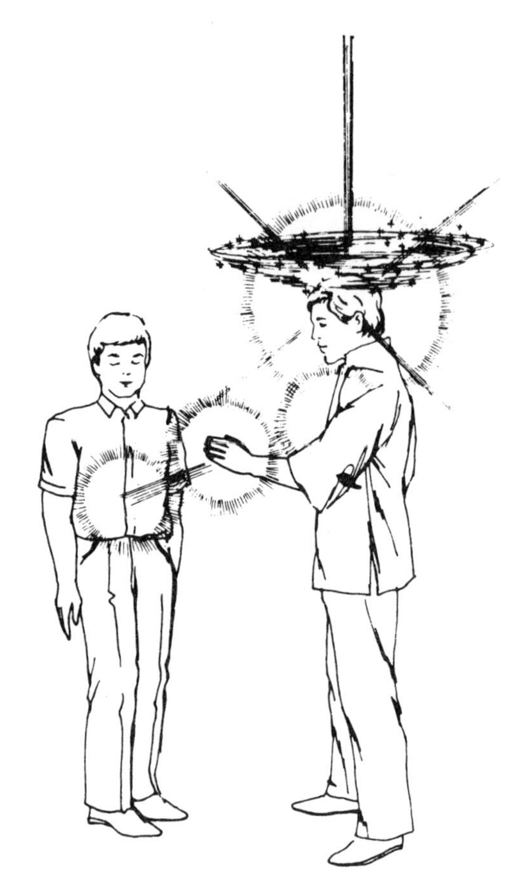

Figure 5. Advanced energizing technique.

CROWN/HAND-CHAKRA TECHNIQUE

To project violet pranic energy when sweeping or energizing, the crown/hand-chakra technique is used. The crown chakra is the receiving chakra while the hand chakra is the giving out or projecting chakra. See figure 6. Pranic healing energy from your Higher Self (or your soul) and air prana are drawn and absorbed by the crown chakra and projected through your hand chakra. The soul pranic energy is electric violet or electric white, and golden yellow in color. Electric violet pranic energy appears as dazzling white or electric white with very light violet or bluish violet. How much soul pranic energy can be drawn depends

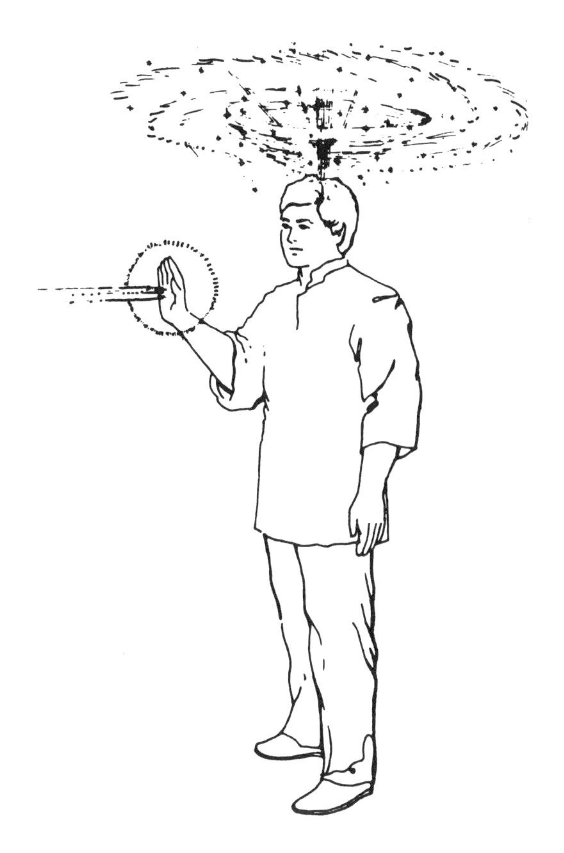

Figure 6. Crown/hand-chakra technique.

upon the spiritual development of the practitioner. The more developed the practioner, the bigger the crown chakra and the thicker the *spiritual cord* that connects the crown and the Higher Self. In an ordinary person, the spiritual cord is hardly visible. This spiritual cord is called the *pillar of light* in the Kaballah, and *antakharana* in Sanskrit (which means a spiritual bridge of light).

The healing energy from the Higher Self is called *heaven ki or energy* in the Taoist tradition, and the *Holy Spirit* in the Christian tradition. Please note, there are two types of violet pranic energy–ordinary violet pranic energy, and electric violet pranic energy.

The crown/hand-chakra technique is simple and easy to learn. The practitioner must do the Meditation on Twin Hearts every day for about fifteen minutes.[3] A beginner must not over-meditate since the energy that will be generated is too strong and will weaken the physical body. This is why many saints have weak physical bodies. This meditation can be gradually lengthened after several months to allow the physical body enough time to adjust to the higher soul energy. The student must practice the Meditation on Twin Hearts, and the crown/hand-chakra technique for at least one month to gain proficiency in projecting violet pranic energy. It is also assumed that the practitioner has earlier achieved proficiency in intermediate pranic healing.

1) Concentrate on the crown chakra and the hand chakra simultaneously. In other words, focus your attention on top of your head and on the center of the hand that is used when sweeping or energizing. Concentration is done just by feeling the top of your head and the center of your palm.

2) Do not strain or overexert your willpower. Do not visualize the violet pranic energy flowing down from the crown chakra to the hand chakra. This is very strenuous. It will cause your concentration to become erratic. Just visualize light-violet pranic energy or electric white pranic energy (soul energy) coming out of your hand. This is very important.

3) You get better results by just being relaxed and by breathing deeply and comfortably.

4) It is not advisable to use the ajna chakra as the receiving chakra or the source chakra for violet pranic energy. The use of the ajna/hand-chakra technique by powerful and willful healers may create a radical or adverse reaction in the patient. Also, avoid using the crown and ajna chakras simultaneously, because the energy may prove very strong and the patient may get worse.

---

[3] See *Pranic Healing*, p. 244, and this volume, p. 141.

ACTIVATING THE CHAKRAS USING THE BASIC HAND-CHAKRA TECHNIQUE

Some major chakras of a depressed patient are quite slow-moving and very small, and, therefore, have to be activated. This is done by energizing the affected chakras with light-red prana, using the basic hand-chakra technique, and simultaneously willing the chakra to become bigger and more active. In the basic hand-chakra technique, the healer concentrates simultaneously on the basic chakra and the hand chakra. Air prana and ground prana are drawn by the basic chakra and projected out through the hand chakra. The healer has to visualize light-red pranic energy coming out of his hand. See figure 7.

Figure 7. The basic/hand-chakra technique. This technique is used to project light red pranic energy in order to activate a chakra that is underactivated, especially in depressed patients. It also can strengthen weak or depleted patients.

Light-red pranic energy is used to activate the lower chakras—the basic chakra, the sex chakra, the meng mein chakra, and, sometimes, the solar plexus chakra. Light-violet pranic energy or electric violet pranic energy is used to activate the higher and lower chakras.

INHIBITING THE CHAKRAS USING THE THROAT/HAND-CHAKRA TECHNIQUE

In violent patients, some major chakras are overactivated; therefore, they have to be inhibited. This is done by visualizing light-blue pranic energy coming out of your hand, while you simultaneously will the chakras to slow down and become

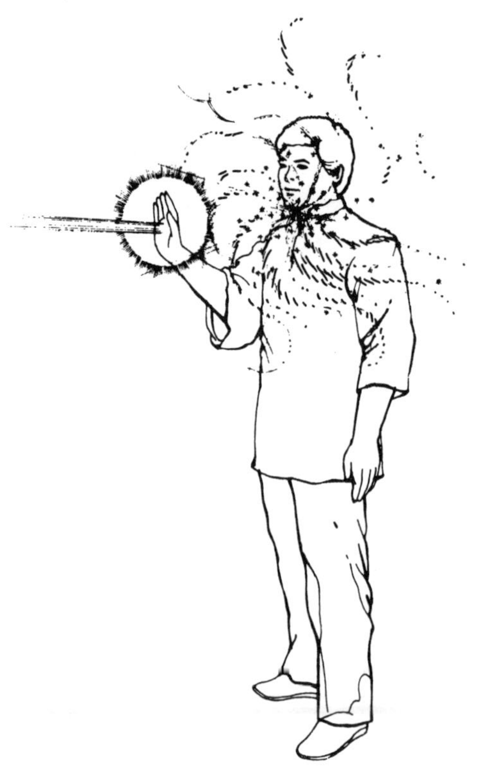

Figure 8. Scanning sideways to determine the size of the chakra.

Figure 9. Throat/hand-chakra technique. This technique is used for projecting blue pranic energy used to inhibit overactive chakras.

smaller. See figure 8. With very violent patients, dark-blue pranic energy has to be applied. The throat/hand-chakra technique (figure 9) is used to project blue pranic energy. Air prana is drawn by the throat chakra and projected through the hand chakra. This is done by concentrating on the throat chakra and the hand chakra simultaneously while visualizing blue pranic energy coming out of the hand chakra. To concentrate means to focus by feeling the throat and the center of the palm simultaneously.

BREATHING MEDITATION OR DEEP PRANIC BREATHING

Emotions affect the solar plexus chakra, which in turn affects the diaphragm; thereby affecting the breathing rhythm. When a person is angry, the movement of the solar plexus chakra becomes erratic, manifesting as an erratic breathing rhythm. By regulating the breathing rhythm, or by practicing slow deep abdominal breathing, the movement of the solar plexus chakra is regulated and harmonized. This produces calmness, peace, and serenity. In other words, you can control your emotions and your mind by controlling your breathing rhythm. By doing slow deep inhalation and exhalation for at least twelve cycles, the solar plexus chakra can be partly normalized; thereby, partially calming down the angry person. Slow deep abdominal breathing can be continued until the person has completely calmed down. Psychotic or violent patients should practice breathing meditation or slow deep abdominal breathing three times daily for about ten to twenty minutes per session to gain greater emotional control. When done daily for several months, the patients will show remarkable improvements. Psychologically imbalanced patients must practice this breathing meditation in order to gain control over the emotions and the mind. The use of breathing exercises to calm and regulate the emotions and the mind is a common practice among yogis and spiritual aspirants. This enables the practitioners to achieve one-pointedness of the mind, serenity, and in some cases expansion of consciousness.

Basically there are two types of breathing–natural and unnatural. When you observe infants breathing, they expand their abdomen when inhaling and contract when exhaling. This is called natural breathing or abdominal breathing. At school, children are taught unnatural (incorrect) breathing or chest breathing. The abdomen contracts and the chest expands while inhaling, and the abdomen expands while exhaling. Chest breathing is unnatural and incorrect for the following reasons:

1) Chest deep breathing–when done for about ten minutes–causes too much pranic energy to gather around the front heart chakra, resulting in pranic congestion of the heart. People who do this will feel dizzy and some discomfort in the chest area. Patients with heart ailments will experience chest pain and a worsening of their condition. When abdominal breathing is done properly, these side effects are not experienced. Some people can even practice for more than one hour per session without experiencing any adverse effects. Instead, they feel stronger, more energized and healthier after such practice.

2) In chest breathing, less air goes into the lungs when the abdomen is contracted during inhalation since the diaphragm is pushed upward; thereby, reducing the space in the lungs. In abdominal breathing, more air goes to the lungs when the abdomen expands during inhalation since the diaphragm is pushed downward; thereby, increasing space in the lungs.

3) As explained earlier, infants and children do abdominal breathing instinctively without being taught, but the breathing pattern is changed when children are taught an incorrect way of breathing in school.

Use the following procedure to develop a new breathing pattern.

1. Do not strain when doing this breathing exercise. You must relax, otherwise you will not be able to do it properly or for long periods.

2. Inhale slowly. Gradually expand your abdomen. Inhalation is done slowly, deeply, and comfortably. Do not overinhale nor overexpand your abdomen. Otherwise your breathing will become erratic, and will defeat the purpose of this breathing technique–which is to produce relaxation and calmness.

3. Hold your breath for a second or two before exhaling. Do not strain–just relax.

4. Exhale slowly. Gradually contract your abdomen. Exhalation is done slowly, deeply, and comfortably. Do not overexhale nor overcontract your abdomen. Otherwise, your breathing will become erratic.

5. Hold your breath for a second or two before inhaling. Do not strain–just relax.

6. Repeat the entire process for about five minutes and gradually extend it to about twenty minutes, or for as long as you like. When doing deep pranic breathing, do not make your breathing too slow–to the extent of becoming strenuous. When your breathing becomes very slow, the chaotic flow of your thoughts will gradually cease. You will experience peace, calmness, and serenity seldom experienced by ordinary people. This slowing down of the breathing must be allowed to manifest gradually without too much strain after long periods of practice.

7. Do physical exercises for about five minutes to release the excess pranic energy and to avoid pranic congestion.

8. Practice deep pranic breathing every day. Normally it takes about three to four sessions before some people can learn to do deep pranic breathing properly. So do not be discouraged if you encounter some slight initial difficulties. If one does not have the patience and perseverance to accomplish small things, then how can one accomplish great things which require greater perseverance and effort? Practice deep pranic breathing every time you are tense or angry. This will calm you down and enable you to regulate and control your emotions and your mind.

If you feel chest pain, discomfort, or dizziness, stop your breathing exercise. You are not doing it properly. Read the instructions carefully and thoroughly. If your breathing becomes erratic, stop and relax for a while before resuming the practice.

MEDITATION ON TWIN HEARTS

When people do the Meditation on Twin Hearts, divine energy flows down to practitioners, filling them with divine light, love, and power. They become a channel to this divine energy. In Taoist yoga, this divine energy is called heaven ki. In Kaballah, this is called the pillar of light because those with clairvoyant faculty literally see a pillar of light. The Indian yogi calls this pillar of light the spiritual bridge of light (or *antakharana*). The Christian calls this the "descent of the Holy Spirit," which is symbolized by a pillar of light with a descending dove. See figure 10 on page 24. In Christian art, this is shown in pictures of saints or Jesus with a pillar of white light on top of the head with a descending white dove. This symbolizes the coming down of the divine energy. Spiritual aspirants who have practiced the Meditation on Twin Hearts for quite some time may experience dazzling light, sometimes even blinding light, or the head filled with dazzling light. This is a common experience among advanced yogis and saints of all religions. If we study the scriptures of different religions, we will notice a similarity among their experiences.

Patients should be instructed to practice deep pranic breathing regularly. Once their minds are sufficiently still, then they can practice the Meditation on Twin Hearts for about fifteen minutes. The Meditation on Twin Hearts can and should be used to heal cases of addiction, depression, and "hallucination" because it facilitates the expelling of negative elementals which are the aggravating factor. You will note the word used is aggravating factor, not the cause, or the causal factor. The cause comes from the patients through their negative thinking, feeling, habits, or karma; they unknowingly attract and allow negative elementals to attach themselves and this results in insanity.

The Meditation on Twin Hearts must be practiced every day for long periods of time in order to become completely healed. But you must remember that patients are the cause of the ailment. They created the negative thought entities. Through negative thinking, feeling, and habits they attract negative elementals,

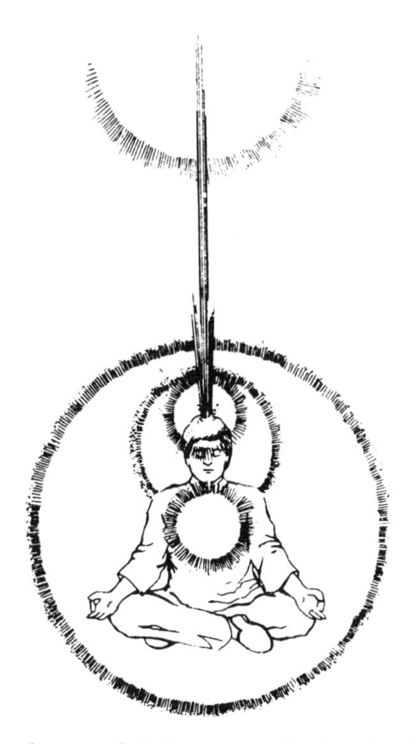

Figure 10. The descent of divine energy during the Meditation on Twin Hearts. In Christian tradition, this is called the Descent of the Holy Spirit; in Taoist Yoga, this is called the Descent of the Heaven Ki; in Kabbalistic tradition–the Pillar of Light; in Indian Yoga–the spiritual bridge of light, or Antakharana.

which cause them to become psychologically ill. Patients must change themselves. They must change their attitude–their way of thinking and feeling. Otherwise, there will be no lasting cure. It is just like a healer who gives pranic treatment to patients with a wound. After the wound is well, the patients would cut themselves again. This is exactly what happens to psychologically ill patients. After the healer has removed the negative thought entities and the negative elementals, the patients create new negative thought entities and attract negative elementals through negative thinking and feeling and this causes a relapse of the ailment. This is why healing has to be repeated for a certain period of time. Patients have to practice slow deep pranic breathing and the Meditation on Twin Hearts in order to hasten the healing process and to gradually improve the character.

If patients practice the Meditation on Twin Hearts daily for several months (or for the rest of their lives), the negative elementals will be prevented from reattaching.

Patients' character will also gradually improve from irritable and violent temperaments to a gentle and kind nature. If the patients are depressed, then they will eventually become happy and optimistic.

POSITIVE THINKING AND FEELING

To hasten the healing process, it is important to instruct patients to maintain a positive attitude–to think, feel, and act positively. Daily positive affirmation is very useful. The healer should create a positive image of these patients, and encourage them to create and maintain a positive self-image, or a positive image of what they can be by using daily positive self-affirmation or positive visualization.

INTEGRATED APPROACH IN PRANIC PSYCHOTHERAPY

Although pranic psychotherapy is very effective and fast in healing psychological ailments, it is better to combine other disciplines of psychotherapy with pranic psychotherapy to produce more effective and lasting results. Pharmacotherapy is very useful, especially in emergency cases. Pranic psychotherapy should be applied before giving counseling. This helps reduce counseling time.

Patients have a tendency to subconsciously "unburden" or transfer the psychologically diseased energy to the counselor, resulting in health problems for the counselor in the long run. By applying pranic psychotherapy first, this is minimized.

KARMA

Knowledge and power are neither good nor bad. It is the motive and the application that determine whether it is good or bad. Because of this, it is necessary to repeat the law of karma in this book. Karma is simply "cause and effect," or what you sow so shall you reap. A person who plants good seeds will harvest good fruits. A person who plants injurious or painful seeds will bear fruits of destruction and suffering. This is inevitable. "God is not to be fooled; a man reaps what he sows" (Galatians 6:7). Never misuse what has been taught in this book, for the karmic repercussion is severe and could reach a hundredfold or more!

There were two possessed people, or to put it in modern parlance, two psychologically imbalanced violent people, who were healed by Jesus. Before they were healed, one of the bad spirits shouted to Jesus, "Have you come here to torment us before our time?" (Matthew 8:28-30). In other words, have you come here to cast us away before the appointed time? From this it is clear that sometimes psychological ailments are karmic in nature and can be healed through divine intercession.

In the past when people were much less educated and were hardly intelligent, esoteric teachings and practices were misunderstood. This is why the townspeople, instead of thanking Jesus for healing the two possessed people who undoubtedly had been causing considerable problems, asked Jesus to leave their town immediately. This indeed is an interesting way of showing gratitude! This is why Jesus taught in parables to the masses, and gave the inner or esoteric teachings and practices to his disciples only (Luke 8:10). Jesus also instructed the disciples not to reveal inner (esoteric) teachings and practices to the unprepared when he told them not to cast their pearls before swine (Matthew 7:6).

REGULAR PRACTICE IS A NECESSITY

Pranic healing is not only a science; it is also an art. In other words, regular practice is very important and the effectiveness of the treatment depends to a great extent on the skill of the healer. It is also advisable to first practice treating mild psychological ailments and gradually work up to more and more difficult cases in order to gain confidence, experience, and skill.

The pranic psychotherapist needs to practice the breathing meditation in order to gain greater emotional and mental stability. The Meditation on Twin Hearts, if practiced daily, will decontaminate you from the patients' diseased energy. It is a common occurrence among psychotherapists to be contaminated with the patients' psychological ailments and they can also become temporarily psychologically imbalanced.

Healing Stress, Irritability, Anxiety, Grief, and Hysteria

Miracles do not happen in contradiction to nature, but only in contradiction to that which is known to us in nature.

–St. Augustine

ONE OF THE MOST common pervasive ailments in modern times is stress or tension. When people are tense, the solar plexus chakra becomes erratic and filled with tense or stressed energy. The crown chakra and the ajna chakra are also partially affected. The health rays are wavy rather than straight and the inner and outer auras are slightly gray in color.

1) Interview the patient. Scan all the major chakras, and apply general sweeping.

2) Apply thoroughly localized sweeping and energizing on the front and back solar plexus chakras with light violet pranic energy or electric white pranic energy by using the crown/hand-chakras technique. Cleansing and energizing should be done alternately until the patient feels a certain degree of relief.

3) Inhibit the overactivated solar plexus chakra by energizing it with light-blue pranic energy, using the throat/hand-chakra technique. Will the solar plexus chakra to normalize.

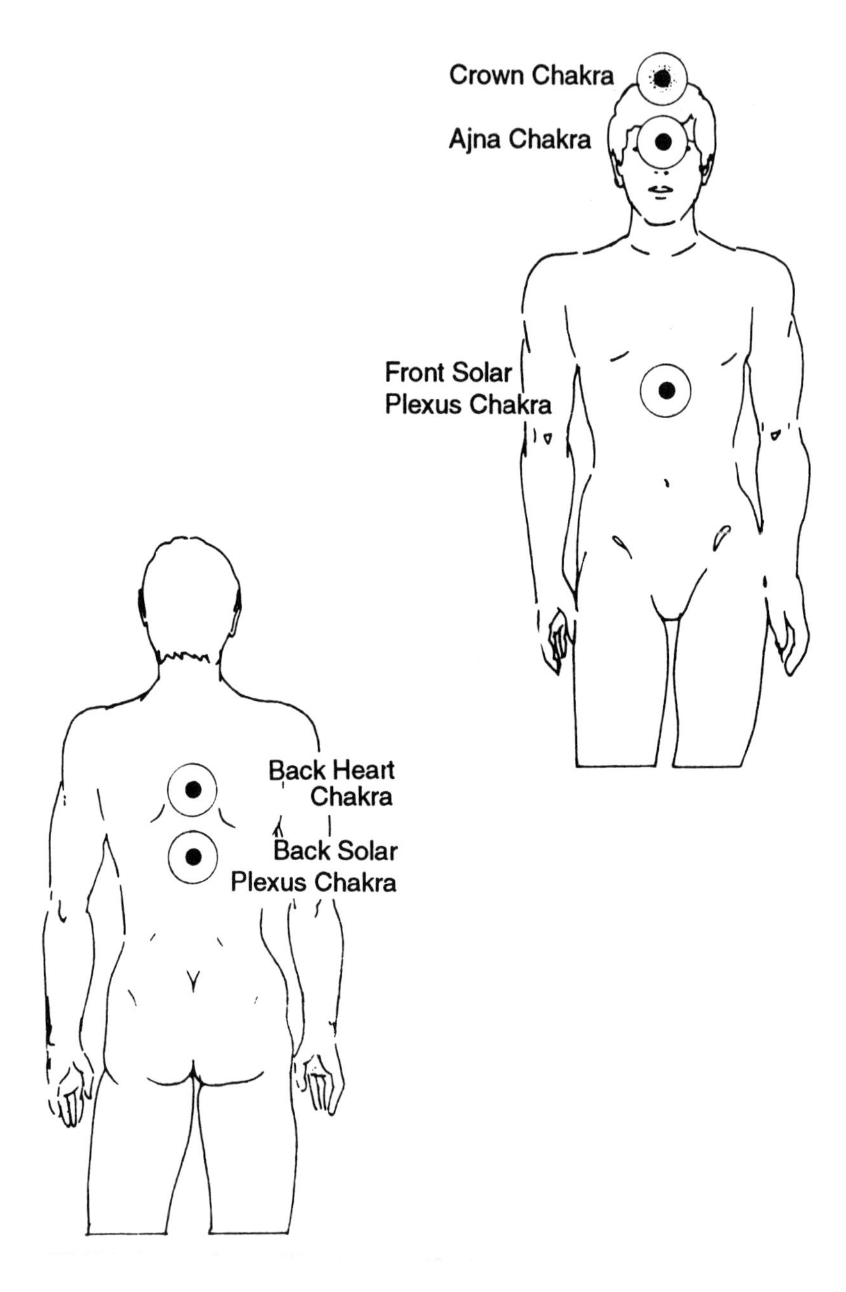

Figure 11. Treatment for stress, tension, irritability, anxiety, grief and hysteria.

4) Apply localized sweeping on the front and back heart chakras. Energize the heart chakra through the back heart chakra with light-violet pranic energy or electric white pranic energy by using the crown/hand-chakra technique. This will produce a soothing and calming effect on the patient. The front heart chakra should not be energized directly because this will cause serious heart congestion. (See figure 11.)

5) The crown chakra and the ajna chakra should be cleansed and energized with light violet pranic energy or electric white pranic energy by using the crown/hand-chakra technique. The purpose is to clean the crown and ajna chakras of negative thoughts and feelings related to stress. It is common for patients who are under stress to experience migraine headaches sometimes for weeks, months or even years. The use of this treatment will usually relieve the patient of his long standing migraine headache. Be sure to thoroughly clean the entire head area before energizing.

You may apply elementary sweeping and energizing techniques. This will also produce good results.

When treating a patient, the healer should be relaxed and not tensed. Otherwise, this tense energy will transfer to the patient. If the treatment is done properly, most patients will experience substantial relief, if not complete relief. It is advisable to teach the patient slow deep abdominal breathing or breathing meditation, and the Meditation on Twin Hearts so he or she can gain emotional and mental control and achieve inner peace.

IRRITABILITY, ANXIETY GRIEF, AND HYSTERIA

Apply the same pranic treatment for tension or stress. Always start with the solar plexus chakra, especially the front solar plexus chakra. By applying cleansing and energizing on this, there will be a noticeable improvement. If the solar plexus chakra is overactivated, then it should be inhibited with light-blue pranic energy using the throat/hand-chakra technique. If the patient is hysterical, the heart chakra should be energized immediately through the back heart chakra, after the solar plexus chakra has been treated. The heart chakra, when energized, produces a calming and soothing effect. For patients suffering from grief, the treatment has to be repeated at least twice a day for several days or weeks. Patients will feel better, but will experience a relapse unless the treatment is repeated.

HOW TO IMPROVE AND SAVE YOUR MARRIAGE

One of the major reasons why some marriages tend to deteriorate is because husband or wife tend to use each other as "psychic garbage cans." The husband or wife usually experiences a lot of stress at work. Since office decorum does not allow emotional outbursts, the spouse, upon returning home, will usually dump or release the stress or psychic garbage on his or her partner and on the children. This will result in a heated exchange of words, and in some cases there may even be physical violence. In the long run, this will contribute to a serious breakdown in the marriage. The children will also be negatively affected and may become psychologically imbalanced. To avoid or minimize these problems, apply regularly pranic psychotherapy on your husband or wife after he or she comes back from work. This will reduce or remove the stress or tension; thereby avoiding or removing any possible heated exchange of words. Even if your partner does not show any external signs of stress, the application of this treatment will produce a feeling of inner peace on your partner which will be highly appreciated, thereby enhancing the relationship.

This treatment can be used on unruly or very temperamental children. It can also be applied in the office, or when important decisions have to be made. By removing the tension or stress, decisions can be made more objectively and quickly. Heated conversations can be calmed down or reduced.

SELF-PRANIC HEALING FOR TENSION, IRRITABILITY, GRIEF, AND ANXIETY

1) Do slow deep abdominal breathing or a breathing meditation until you feel normalized. This may take from ten to thirty minutes. You can do abdominal breathing while at work or while undergoing tremendous work stress. Abdominal breathing has soothing, calming, and energizing effects. This is very useful for people living in developed countries where the work pace is very fast and the stress level is very high.

2) Or apply localized sweeping and energizing alternately on the front solar plexus chakra until you feel relieved. Apply localized sweeping and energizing on the crown and ajna chakra. You can do abdominal breathing while sweeping and energizing.

3) Do the Meditation on Twin Hearts. If practiced properly, the results will be very amazing and very fast. You can achieve deep inner peace and objectivity by performing it. This can also help improve marriage relationships, especially if both husband and wife practice the meditation daily.

4) Practice positive self-imaging regularly. Visualize the stressful condition. Look at it detachedly and objectively. Visualize that you are calm and doing the right thing. Do abdominal breathing when doing positive self-imaging. Repeat this every day until your reaction to the situation has improved. When you visualize the stressful condition and look at it detachedly and objectively, you are already partially releasing the stress energy in your chakras. Also when you visualize that you are calm and doing the right thing, you are actually creating positive thought entities

which will condition you to react positively to the "stressful" condition. What we call stress is nothing more than our negative reaction to a taxing situation.

It is advisable to practice a breathing meditation and the Meditation on Twin Hearts every day in order to achieve control and to gain skill in stilling the emotions and the mind.

It is difficult to think objectively and clearly when you are irritated, angry, or tense. This will, of course, detrimentally affect the quality of the decisions you make. Therefore, it is advisable to practice self-pranic psychotherapy while at work, or to ask an officemate to apply pranic psychotherapy on you to reduce tension or stress; thereby, increasing your productivity.

SEXUAL IMPOTENCE

Sexual impotence may be due to physical or psychological factors, or both. Patients suffering from sexual impotence have depleted sex chakra and navel chakras. The basic chakra may also be depleted. If this is due to psychological factors, then the solar plexus chakra, the heart chakra, ajna chakra, and the crown chakra have to be treated. See figure 12.

1) Interview the patient.

2) Scan and apply general sweeping.

3) Apply localized sweeping on the basic chakra, sex chakra, and navel chakra.

4) Energize these chakras with light-red pranic energy by using the basic hand chakra technique. If the patient is afflicted with venereal disease or has had history of venereal disease, then do not apply this treatment and do not use red pranic energy because it will aggravate the venereal disease, or it may activate the dormant germs.

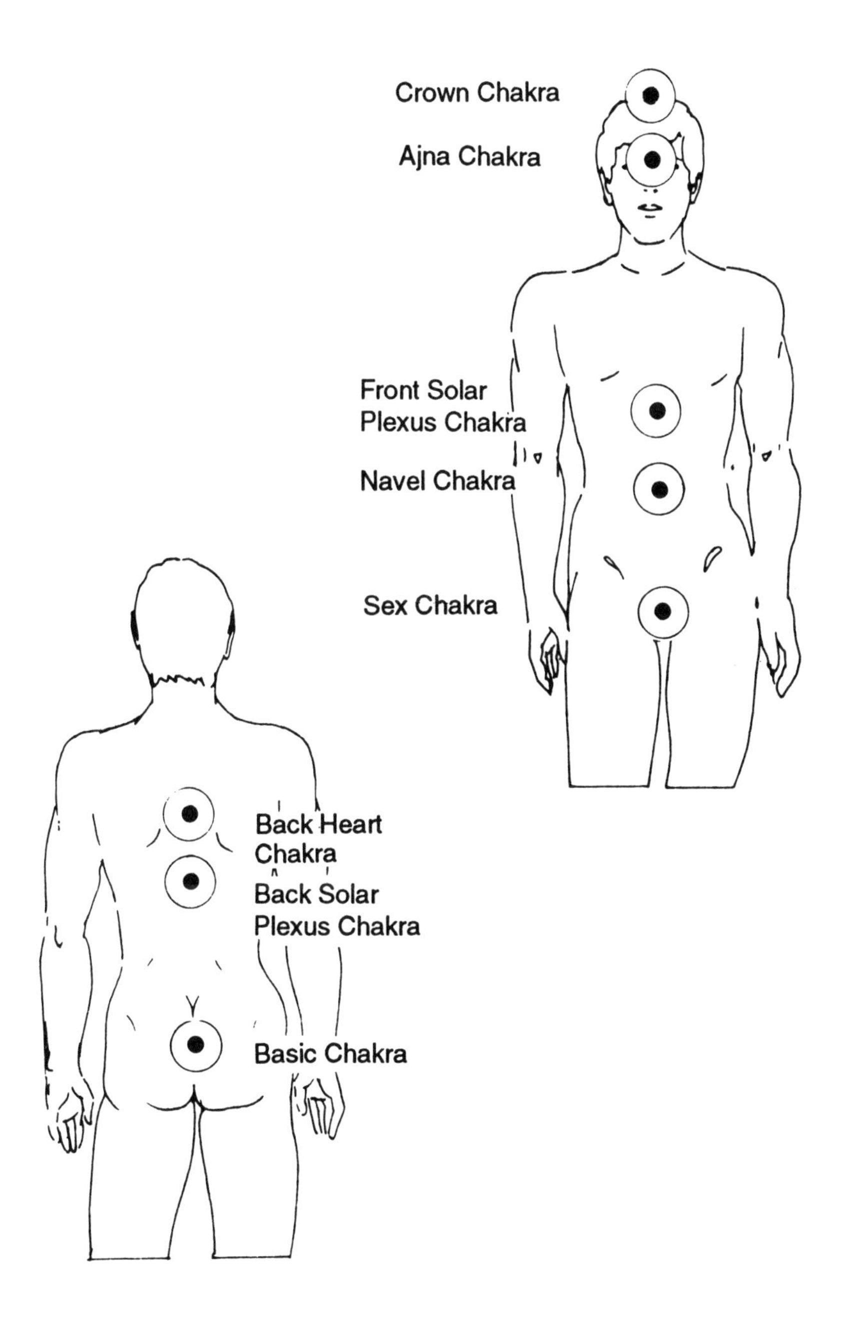

Figure 12. Treatment for sexual impotence and frigidity.

5) Clean and energize the solar plexus chakra, the ajna chakra, and the crown chakra with light-violet pranic energy by using the crown/hand-chakra technique. While localized sweeping is applied on these chakras, the healer must form an intention to remove the stress energy or negative energy lodged in the chakras.

6) Inhibit the overactivated solar plexus chakra by energizing with light-blue pranic energy, using the throat/hand-chakra technique.

7) Clean and energize the heart chakra through the back heart chakra using light-violet pranic energy with the crown/hand-chakra technique. Repeat the treatment twice a week.

If the treatment is done properly, there should be substantial improvement within a month or two in most cases. The patient should be instructed to practice sexual abstinence for some time after he has become potent again to regulate sexual activity. Otherwise, the sex chakra might become depleted again.

SELF-PRANIC TREATMENT FOR SEXUAL IMPOTENCE

1) Apply sweeping and energizing on your basic chakra, sex chakra, navel chakra, solar plexus chakra, ajna chakra, and crown chakra by using the hand-chakra technique. This may take ten to twenty minutes. Do this every day.

2) Do the Meditation on Twin Hearts every day. Self-pranic treatment should be continued for several months, even if there is already substantial improvement. Otherwise, there might be a relapse.

TESTIMONIALS

My husband experiences a lot of stress at work. He has pain in the solar plexus and heart after coming from work. At times he gets depressed or easily gets angry or irritated. After pranic treatment, he is relieved and at one time he even described it as blissful.

Date:	August, 1988
Name:	Riza Regis
Address:	4 Nueva Ecija St. Philam, Las Piñas, Metro Manila
Case:	*Work tension*

The patient (C.C.N.) is a temperamental person. At about 10:00 P.M. August 8, 1988, she got angry with someone. The more she thought about it, the angrier she became. Distant pranic healing was applied. As a result, she became calmer and went to sleep. The next day her anger was gone.

Date:	August 10, 1988
Name:	Sia Hian Eng
Address:	754 Calero St. Sta. Cruz, Manila
Case:	*Anger*

For ten days, I experienced colds, cough, headaches, and gum aches due to the tremendous stress in connection with a big business project that we were undertaking. Being a student of pranic healing, I decided to apply self-pranic healing. This was done by doing pranic breathing or abdominal breathing, and applying cleansing and energizing on the front solar plexus chakra and the affected parts. Before treatment, I felt drowsy and felt pain in my head and in my gums. After self-pranic treatment, the pain was completely gone. I was emotionally at peace and was able to look at the situation in a more detached and objective manner.

Date:	September 1, 1988
Name:	Robert Marin
Address:	503 F. Policarpio St. Mandaluyong, Metro Manila
Case:	*Stress*

Before treatment I was fearful, mentally disturbed, easily got nervous, had difficulty sleeping, and had nightmares for three years. After being treated twice a week for about two months, I feel much better physically, emotionally, and spiritually. My fear and nervousness were lessened considerably, and my attitude is now more positive.

Date:	September 1, 1988
Name:	Manny Castro
Age:	35
Address:	670 Edsa, Pasay City
Case:	*Anxiety*

The most significant thing that occurred in one of the meditations I experienced took place only two days ago. I felt very low because I felt anger and hatred for my husband. I felt he was cheating on me. The whole night I was full of remorse and anger. It kept me awake and crying. After realizing I was not getting anywhere, I did the Meditation on Twin Hearts. It was four in the morning. It was a tremendous experience because after doing it, I felt my whole being filled with love, understanding, and peace. I lost all the hatred and anger that I had felt for my husband. And when he finally came home, he assured me without my asking that he was true and faithful to me.

Date:	September 10, 1988
Name:	S.M.B.
Address:	Withheld
Occupation:	Housewife and Businesswoman
Case:	*Anger*

On a Friday night, I got a call from a friend, Bob, requesting me to reserve the function room of a nearby coffeeshop the following day, Saturday, from 1:00 P.M. to 5:00 P.M. I inquired why and he said he will have a confrontation with his wife, who walked out on him. She was bringing a lawyer along to ask for support for their children. I asked him how he felt about these things, and he said he was very nervous, anxious, depressed, and, of course, very angry. So I said that it's important that he gets a good sleep and keeps calm so he can think well. He asked me how, since the mere thought of a confrontation made him very restless. So I said that I would do distant pranic healing on him. I told him to keep quiet for about ten minutes, to close his eyes and pray that everything turns out well the next day.

For ten minutes, I swept his aura with violet light. I energized his crown, ajna, throat and solar plexus chakras with blue and violet light, too.

The next morning, I called him to ask whether he was able to sleep. He said that in less than 10 minutes, he was "out of this world" and he woke up at 6:30 A.M. feeling very well rested. But later, he was very nervous and angry again. I dictated to him to pray "God is almighty, God is merciful. He is healing me of my anxiety, in full faith and trust, so be it." I told him to repeat this mentally the whole afternoon, while he and his wife faced each other. He did pray and he said that every time his wife raised her voice, he would start praying the self-affirmation.

They settled their problem that afternoon, without any violence and rantings, and he told me that the pranic healing and prayer did really affect his disposition to be more calm.

Patient: B.Z.
Address: B.F. Homes, Paranaque
Healer: Bienvenida S. Bernas
Case: *Marital Stress*

I went back to Heidi's store to return merchandise. I noticed that she was upset because she was breathless as she was talking. I really don't know her that well, but perhaps she was really so uncomfortable that's why she said that she had pain in her stomach. I offered to heal her. She was depleted in the heart, ajna, crown, solar plexus, and also the basic chakras. I applied a thorough sweeping of the whole body. While I was sweeping her, I noticed that she was teary-eyed. I energized all the depleted areas with violet light. After 10 minutes, I asked her how she felt and she said that she felt an inner peace.

Before I went home, she was already smiling and she said that she will talk to her daughter about their problem. They had an argument that morning and she was intimated by her daughter, a teenager, for some time already.

I left her store, feeling fine because I made somebody happy.

Patient:	Heidi V.
Address:	San Juan, Rizal
Healer:	Bienvenida S. Bernas
Case:	*Family Stress*

Richard, 15 years old, was referred to us by his parents, because he plucked his eyebrows, and for some time had been continually plucking his hair, which left small bald spots on his head. He was suspected of being under the influence of drugs and was being accused of stealing money at home. On scanning, I found that his solar and navel chakras were both congested. Later, he confessed that he felt deeply hurt about being accused of stealing for he said he never did. Further, he claimed feeling alone and insecure because he missed his parents as they both worked abroad. After pranic healing–combined with conventional support psychotherapy–he experienced relief and felt emotionally better.

Date:	October 5, 1988
Healer:	Dr. Sonia L. Dy
Address:	Metropolitan Hospital Masangkay Street, Sta. Cruz Metro Manila
Occupation:	Psychiatrist and pranic psychotherapist
Case:	*Anxiety*

DF consulted me with complaints of feeling tense, anxious, and fearful about the side effects her medicine for asthma might cause her body. In lieu of an interview, I opted to scan the patient and immediately informed her that she seemed to be suppressing a lot of her feelings. The patient was surprised that I knew this when she had not told me anything yet. I explained how feelings affect the energy centers or chakras and demonstrated to her how her navel chakra was congested. After the explanation, she readily talked about her feelings. She confided that she found difficulty in expressing her feelings toward her family, particularly in demonstrating affection for fear of being rejected. This caused her extreme anxiety, depression, and feelings of insecurity. I proceeded with pranic psychotherapy, and after the session the patient felt relieved, relaxed, and claimed, "Guminhawa na ang pakiramdam ko" ("I felt relieved"). She added that before coming in for therapy, she felt a terrible sense of hopelessness but after the session, Nawala na ang ko at nabuhayan ako ng loob. ("My worries were gone and I felt a new surge of courage.")

Date:	November 29, 1988
Healer:	Dr. Sonia L. Dy
Address:	Metropolitan Hospital Masangkay Street, Sta. Cruz Metro Manila
Occupation:	Psychiatrist and pranic psychotherapist
Case:	*Anxiety*

This is a case of a business executive–a middle manager in a highly competitive business who consulted me because he was suffering from insomnia, migraines, heaviness on the chest, and severe physical exhaustion. It was discovered that the reasons for these were the pressures and demands of work which laid heavily on his shoulders. When I scanned the patient, I found that his solar plexus and navel chakras were congested. After applying pranic psychotherapy, the patient felt relieved.

Date:	November 29, 1988
Healer:	Dr. Sonia L. Dy
Address:	Metropolitan Hospital Masangkay Street, Sta. Cruz Metro Manila
Case:	*Anxiety*

Healing Phobias, Traumas, Obsessions, and Compulsions

Healing is brought about by releasing or removing the negative pent-up psychic energy within the patient.

–C.K.S.

Thoughts are real. Repeated negative thoughts and feelings in the long run produce obsessive ideas and may precipitate into compelling negative actions. Repeated negative actions in the long run produce compulsive behaviour. Removal or cleansing of the accumulated negative thoughts and feelings results in rapid healing of the psychologically ill patient.

–C.K.S.

PHOBIA IS nothing more than a traumatic experience or a fear energy embedded on the solar plexus, crown and/or ajna chakras. The emphasis should be on the crown chakra and the solar plexus chakra since the traumatic energy or fear energy usually lodges in these two chakras or centers. See figure 13 on page 44.

1) Apply sweeping on the crown chakra, solar plexus chakra and the ajna chakra with light-violet or electric violet pranic energy by

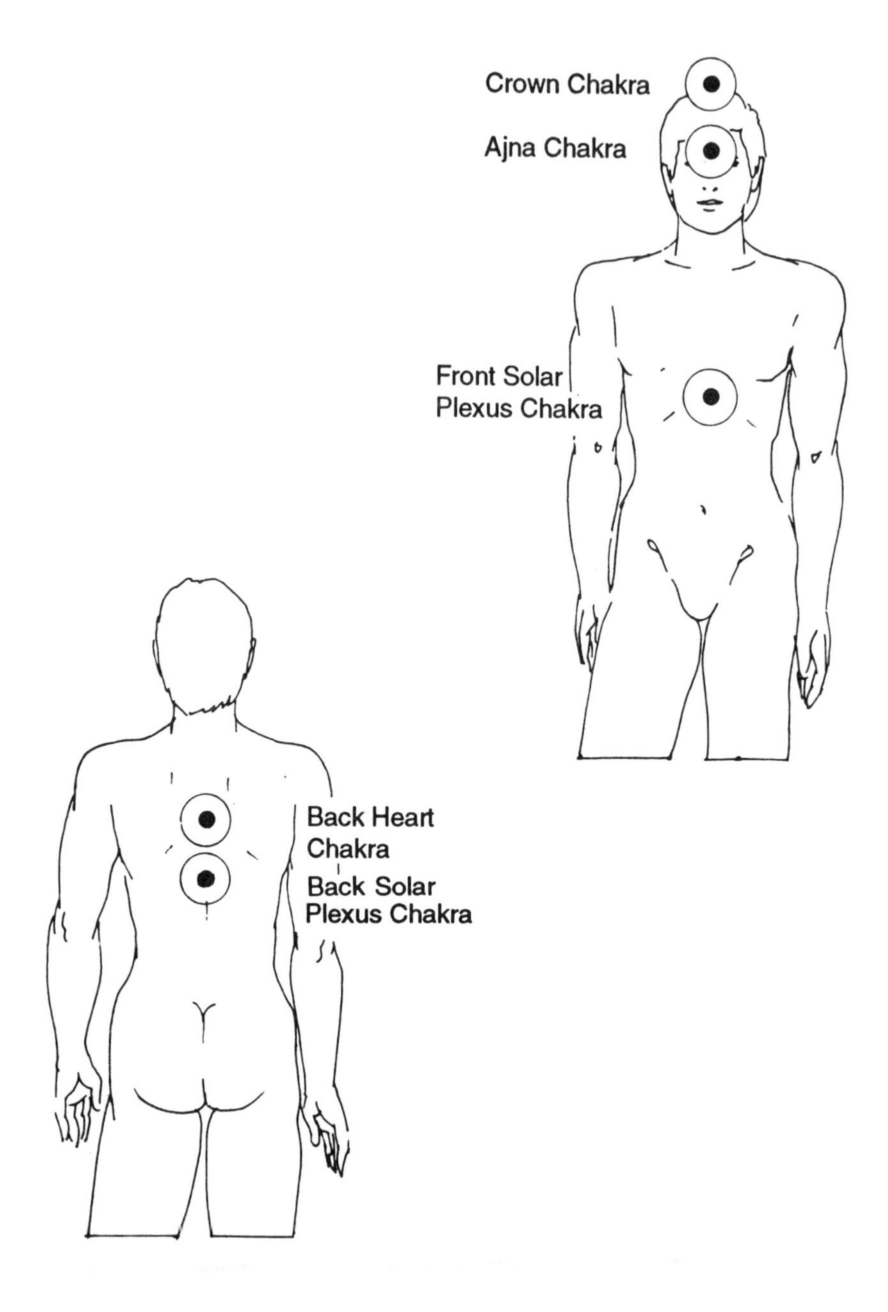

Figure 13. Treatment for phobias, traumas, obsessions, and uncontrollable compulsions.

using the crown/hand-chakra technique with the intention of removing and disintegrating the traumatic or fear energy. If done properly, there should be noticeable or substantial improvement.

2) Clean the heart chakra, and energize it through the back heart chakra with light-violet or electric violet pranic energy by using the crown/hand-chakra technique.

3) Repeat the treatment once or twice a week until the patient is completely relieved.

STUTTERING

Apply the same treatment as for phobia. The throat chakra and the secondary throat chakra have to be cleansed and energized with light-violet or electric violet pranic energy by using the crown/hand-chakra technique. Repeat the treatment twice a week.

OBSESSIONS AND UNCONTROLLABLE COMPULSIONS

The treatment is the same as phobia, except that the intention is to remove the obsessive thought or thoughts.

COMPULSIVE EATING

With compulsive eaters, the front solar plexus chakra is partially cracked and has several elementals embedded on it. The throat chakra and the secondary throat chakra are also affected. See figure 14 on page 46.

In order to remove the negative elementals and the thought entities related to compulsive eating, and to seal the cracks on the protective webs, clean and energize with light-violet or electric

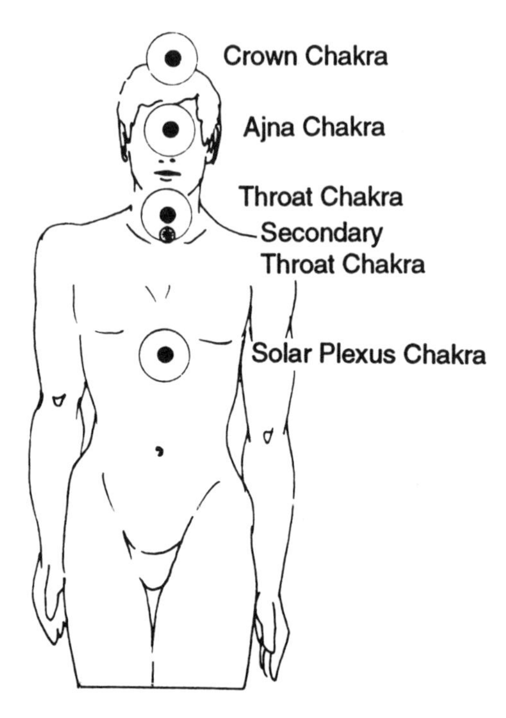

Figure 14. Treatment for compulsive eating.

violet pranic energy on the solar plexus, throat, secondary throat, ajna, and crown chakras by using the crown/hand-chakra technique. Repeat treatment until the patient is well.

NYMPHOMANIA, EXHIBITIONISM, SEXUAL VIOLENCE AND CHILD MOLESTING

To have sexual urges or desires is very healthy. Sex is a joyful activity. One should not feel any guilt about it. It should not be repressed, but rather should be regulated. For advanced esoteric students, sex energy can be transmuted to increase creativity, to improve health, or to hasten spiritual development. See figure 15.

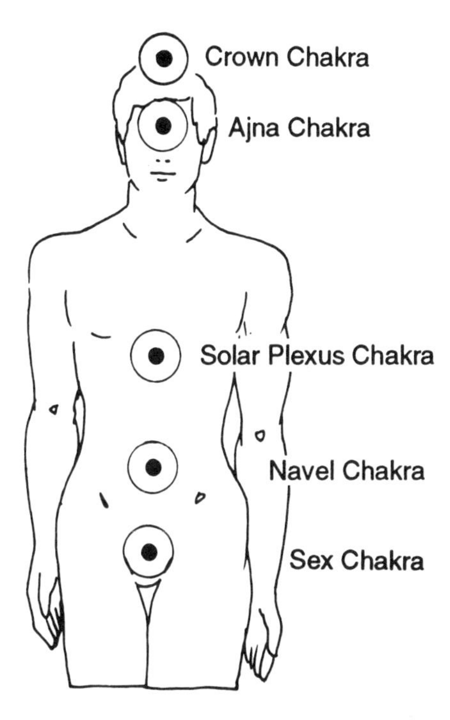

Figure 15. Treatment for sexual ailments, exhibitionism, sexual violence, and child molesting.

1) Clean and energize with light-violet or electric violet pranic energy on the sex, navel, solar plexus, ajna, and crown chakras by using the crown/hand-chakra technique. When sweeping is applied, you must will to remove the negative elementals and the negative thought entities on the sex chakra, solar plexus chakra, ajna chakra and crown chakra. The sex chakra and the solar plexus chakra have cracks and are filled with negative elementals. Sometimes the ajna chakra and the crown chakra are also affected. The obsessive idea or thought entities have to be removed from the crown chakra, ajna chakra and the solar plexus chakra.

2) The sex chakra and solar plexus chakra are overactivated. Therefore, they have to be inhibited by energizing with blue pranic energy by using the throat/hand-chakra technique. You

must will the sex chakra and the solar plexus chakra to reduce to two-and-a-half inches in diameter. Repeat the treatment several times a week.

COMPLEMENTARY SELF-PRANIC TREATMENT FOR PHOBIAS, TRAUMAS, AND OTHER PSYCHOLOGICAL AILMENTS

As explained earlier, pranic healing is based on two basic principles–cleansing and energizing. The psychological healing process is accelerated by cleansing oneself of traumatic energy, negative habits, negative thoughts and feelings. This is done by "externalizing and disintegrating the accumulated negative thoughts and feelings, or negative thought entities within oneself" in the form of phobia, traumas, obsessive ideas, compulsive behavior, addiction, and depressing thoughts or feelings.

EXTERNALIZING AND DISINTEGRATING NEGATIVE THOUGHT ENTITIES

1) Relax and do abdominal breathing.

2) Externalize the traumatic experience, phobia, depressing thoughts, bad habits, or negative thoughts and feelings. This is done by visualizing a white board and projecting your phobia or the negative thoughts and feelings on it. The visualization does not have to be clear. What is important is the intention.

3) Disintegrate the accumulated negative thoughts and feelings in the form of negative thought entities by just simply erasing them on the white board. The intention and the act of disintegrating the negative thought entities is symbolized by the act of the erasing.

4) Repeat the entire process several times until you feel substantially relieved. Repeat the treatment several times within the next few weeks.

5) Another way of externalizing and disintegrating the accumulated negative thoughts and feelings in the form of negative thought entities is to visualize a boiling cauldron. Throw all your psychic garbage into it.

6) You can also visualize a piece of white bond paper in front of you and project the accumulated negative thoughts and feelings in the form of negative thought entities on the paper. Visualize that the paper, together with the negative thought entities, is thrown to an electric violet fire. The externalization of the negative thought entities is partial; therefore, the process has to be repeated several times.

7) Instead of disintegrating the negative thought entity, you can transmute it. This is done by visualizing and feeling the thought entity transforming into something positive. Or you can recall very happy events in your life. Project and mix this happy experience with the negative thought entity, thereby transforming it into something positive.

CLEANSING YOUR OWN NEGATIVE ELEMENTALS

After cleansing yourself of accumulated negative thoughts and feelings in the form of negative entities, it is still necessary to clean away negative elementals. This is done by simply doing the Meditation on Twin Hearts regularly and properly. The soul energy, or the electric violet pranic energy coming down, will expel the negative elementals and will seal the cracks or holes in the protective webs.

For people who are not eighteen years old, or who have certain types of physical ailments that do not allow them to practice the Meditation of Twin Hearts, practice meditation on the white light.

CREATING A POSITIVE SELF-IMAGE

The healing process is further hastened by "energizing" yourself with positive thoughts and feelings. This is done by positive affirmation or positive self-imaging. The positive affirmation has to be done every day, for about ten minutes a day, for at least several months. Persistence is very important in order to produce strong positive thoughts of yourself.

Another way of producing strong positive thoughts is by positive self-imaging or creative visualization. If you are depressed, then you should visualize yourself as being happy, optimistic, and filled with enthusiasm. Or if you have the tendency to be violent, then visualize yourself as being gentle, calm, and objective under tense or provoking situations. The visualization has to be done every day for about ten minutes a day for at least several months. The visualization does not have to be clear. Whether your visualization is clear or not, it does not affect the potency of the thoughts produced. What is necessary is to have a clear persistent *intention*. Clear intention means to have a clear idea of what you want to be. Persistence means to maintain the clear intention or visualization for at least ten minutes and to do this for several months. You will be able to create powerful positive thought entities which will have a supportive influence on you. It is preferable to do pranic breathing while visualizing to make the thought entity more powerful. Your concentration does not have to be perfect. What is required is to bring back your attention to what you are visualizing every time your mind drifts to something else.

The pranic psychotherapist can hasten the healing process of the patient by creating a positive image of the patient through creative visualization, and by thinking and feeling positively and kindly toward the patient. The visualization has to be done for five to ten minutes per session, several times a week, and for as long as necessary. The pranic psychotherapist or psychiatrist must preferably do pranic breathing while visualizing to make the thought entity more powerful.

TESTIMONIALS

I had a very strong phobia for lightning, strong rain, and wind. I suffered from this for about twenty years and it was no joke. Just seeing the sky getting dark would make my knees tremble. I would start to get cold hands and feet, and have severe stomach trouble, gas pain, and frequent urination. My heart beat loudly and very fast, and I had difficulty breathing. So the longer the rain and lightning, the longer my suffering. What was worse was that I could not work, eat, or think those times. I prayed and tried to explain my situation away to myself, just to be relieved of the suffering because that was how desperate I was. I was terribly frightened.

My prayer was answered when I met Master Choa. He healed me during the workshop on advanced pranic healing. He asked a lady doctor who was a clairvoyant–Dra. Luna–to monitor my chakras. He cleansed and energized my crown and solar plexus chakras.

The test came after a month when the strong typhoon "Unsang" hit the country. In the past, just hearing about an incoming typhoon would simply change my body chemistry. This time it was also the same, although to a lesser degree. When the rain and the wind started to come, I was surprised to feel that my fear did not magnify in relation to the strong rain. The little fear that I felt at the start gradually disappeared in spite of the fact that the rain and wind did not weaken. I was still able to go out with my brother to heal his grandson who had a very high fever since I had then already learned how to heal. This was how I found out that I was really healed of my phobia.

Date:	November 19, 1988
Name:	Angelita C. Santos
Address:	61-A Mabilis St. Diliman Quezon City
Occupation:	Businesswoman
Case:	*Phobia*

Healing Addiction: Smoking, Alcoholism, and Drug Addiction

You must understand that it is very difficult to be sincere with yourself. A man is very much afraid of seeing the truth.

–Gurdjieff

THE SOLAR plexus chakra of smokers, alcoholics, and drug addicts is affected. Cleansing and energizing this chakra is very important and will cause substantial improvement, since the solar plexus chakra is the center of the desire or craving.

SMOKING

With mild smokers, only the throat chakra and the secondary throat chakra are affected. Their protective webs have cracks with negative elementals embedded in them. These smoker elementals can be clairvoyantly seen as small orange flames with muddy red cores. With heavy smokers, the solar plexus chakra is affected with the smoker's many negative elementals on it. In some cases even the ajna and crown chakras are affected. Heavy smokers have more negative and bigger elementals than mild smokers.

In order to heal smokers, the negative elementals and the thought entities created by the desire to smoke have to be removed. These negative thought entities are predominantly located on the front solar plexus chakra and the crown chakra. Cleansing and energizing with violet pranic energy will have to be done in order to expel the remaining negative elementals and negative thought entities related to smoking, and to seal the cracks on the protective webs. Pranic treatments have to be repeated two to three times a week because of possible relapse.

For the patients to get well, they must have a certain degree of determination to give up smoking. Otherwise the patients will only experience a certain degree of relief from the urge to smoke but may revert back to smoking within a very short period of time. These negative elementals are really weak. They are just like

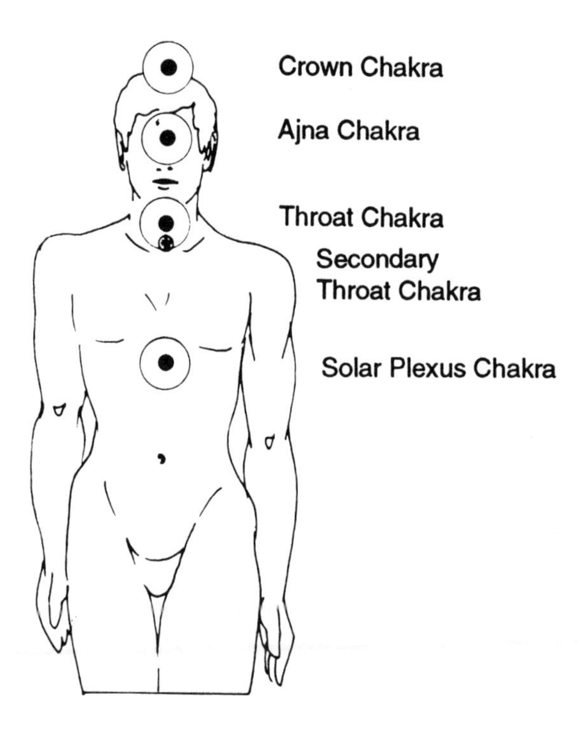

Figure 16. Treatment for smoking and alcoholism.

etheric insects or cockroaches. You can overcome them just by simply willing not to smoke. I have personally encountered several people who gave up smoking immediately by just an act of the will without undergoing pranic treatment. See figure 16.

1) Apply localized sweeping with light-violet or electric violet pranic energy by using the crown/hand-chakra technique on the throat area–front, right side, and left side. Sweeping must be done very thoroughly.

2) The secondary throat chakra must also be cleansed thoroughly. The elementals, as well as the dirty energy, must be thrown into a disposal unit made of water and salt.

3) Energize sufficiently the throat chakra and the secondary throat chakra with light violet or electric violet pranic energy by using the crown/hand-chakra technique.

4) Apply localized sweeping and energizing on the front and back solar plexus chakra, ajna chakra and the crown chakra with light violet or electric violet pranic energy by using the crown/hand-chakra technique.

5) When sweeping, there must be an intention to remove the negative elementals and the negative thought entities. It is advisable for the smoker to regularly practice slow deep abdominal breathing. This is to help overcome stress.

ALCOHOLISM

When a person has an uncontrollable desire to drink, this is because there are bigger elementals deeply embedded on the solar plexus chakra, as well as on the throat chakra and secondary throat chakra. The size of these elementals varies. In some cases it is about three or four inches in diameter, the shape is inchoate, and the color is muddy red. Based on this observation, it is quite clear that red is the color for desire.

The pranic treatment for alcoholics is almost the same as for smokers (see figure 16). The emphasis is on the front solar plexus chakra and this chakra is treated first. The healer should closely monitor the progress of the patient. The treatment should be continued for as long as necessary. It is very important to help the patient solve his or her emotional problems. The patient needs to have a certain degree of intention to give up drinking. It is also very important to give up old drinking companions and to develop new friends. Joining some sort of a group or association–especially religious or spiritual ones–would be very helpful.

DRUG ADDICTION

In the case of drug addicts, the elementals are even bigger and more powerful. They are muddy red in color. With addicts, it is not only cracks on the etheric web, but big punctures or big holes. The protective webs of the solar plexus chakra, throat chakra, secondary throat chakra, ajna chakra, and crown chakra are punctured. Because of the big holes, the patient has visual and auditory hallucinations, or hears strange voices. The protective webs of the ear chakras have to be treated. If the patient is restless and cannot sleep, the protective web of the basic chakra has to be treated.

With drug addict patients, the energy body is depleted. The basic chakra, navel chakra, spleen chakra, and the solar plexus chakra are depleted. This is the major reason why addicts feel such a strong urge to use drugs. These chakras have to be cleansed and energized.

The treatment for drug addicts is divided into two parts. The first part is to remove the addiction and hallucination by removing the negative elementals and negative thought entities, and to heal or seal the wounds of the protective webs by energizing them. The affected chakras are the solar plexus, throat, secondary throat, ajna, crown, back head, and ears. By cleansing and energizing the solar plexus chakra, the patient will feel a substantial relief from the addiction. See figure 17.

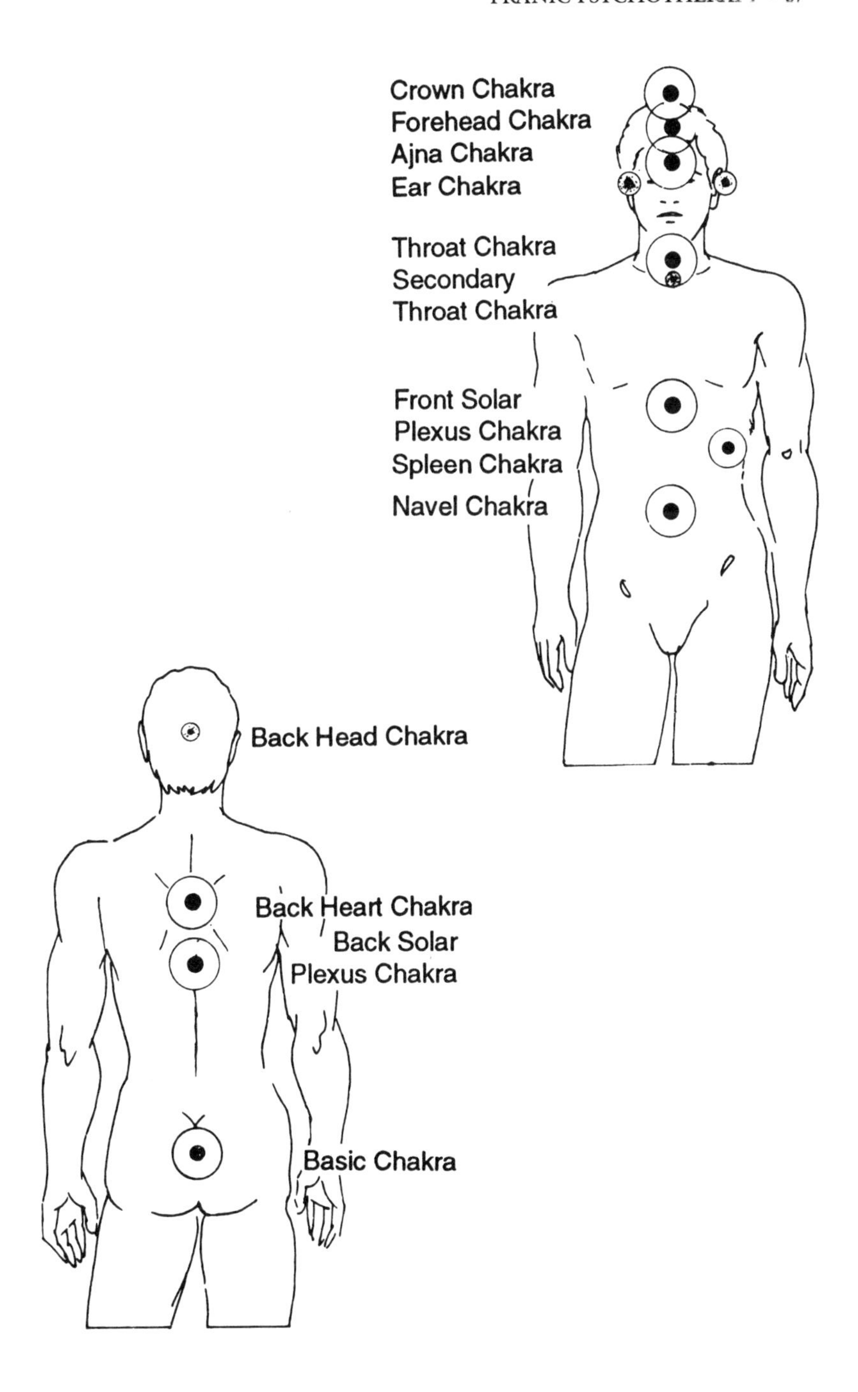

Figure 17. Treatment for drug addiction.

The second part is to reduce the withdrawal symptoms by energizing with light-red pranic energy on the depleted lower chakras—basic chakra, navel chakra, and spleen chakra—by using the basic/hand-chakra technique.

1) Interview the patient and scan the major chakras, the back head chakra, and the ear chakras.

2) Apply general sweeping.

3) Apply localized sweeping and energizing on the front and back solar plexus chakras with light-violet or electric violet pranic energy by using the crown/hand-chakra technique. When sweeping is applied on the solar plexus chakra, there should be an intention to remove and disintegrate the negative elementals and the negative thought entities lodged in it.

4) Apply localized sweeping and energizing on the throat chakra, secondary throat chakra, ajna chakra, forehead chakra, crown chakra, back head chakra, and ear chakras with light-violet or electric violet pranic energy by using the crown/hand-chakra technique. The protective webs of these chakras usually have cracks or holes with negative elementals embedded in them, except the forehead chakra—which is just partially depleted. These will substantially reduce the urge or addiction and the hallucination.

5) Apply localized sweeping and energizing on the back heart chakra with light-violet or electric violet pranic energy by using crown/hand-chakra technique to produce peace and harmony within the patient.

6) Apply cleansing and energizing on the basic chakra, navel chakra, and the spleen chakra with light red pranic energy by using the basic/hand-chakra technique. This will substantially reduce the depression or the withdrawal symptoms.

7) The treatment should be done at least once every two days. The frequency of the treatment can be increased if necessary. The

patient may feel very light and free from the urge, and may think that he or she is already completely cured. The healer should definitely instruct the patient to come back for more treatments, because there is a high probability of relapse after several days. The treatment should be continued for at least one to two months or longer.

For drug users, a change of companions is definitely very important. If possible, they should change their residence. Also, joining a religious or spiritual group would be very advantageous.

HALLUCINATION AND RESTLESSNESS

Hallucination simply means seeing or hearing something that is not physically present. It does not mean that what is being seen or heard is imaginary. On the contrary, what is being seen or heard is quite real in the inner world. If the person is of lower spiritual development then he or she will attract beings of similar low development, and will see and hear ugly things. Persons who hallucinate have holes in some of their protective webs.

Psychics can open or close their own protective webs—voluntarily or involuntarily. The protective webs do not have holes. Voluntary psychics can open and close the protective webs at will. Involuntary psychics do not have full voluntary control on the opening and closing of the protective webs. Different psychics use different chakras for sensing.

With hallucinating patients, the solar plexus, ajna, crown, back head, and ear chakras are affected. (See figure 18 on page 60.) They have to be cleansed and energized with light-violet or electric violet pranic energy by using the crown/hand-chakra technique. The treatment has to be repeated at least three times a week to avoid relapse, especially if the ailment is of long standing. If the patient is restless and cannot sleep, then the protective web of the basic chakra has cracks and is embedded with negative elementals. The basic chakra has to be treated with light-violet pranic energy by using the crown/hand-chakra technique.

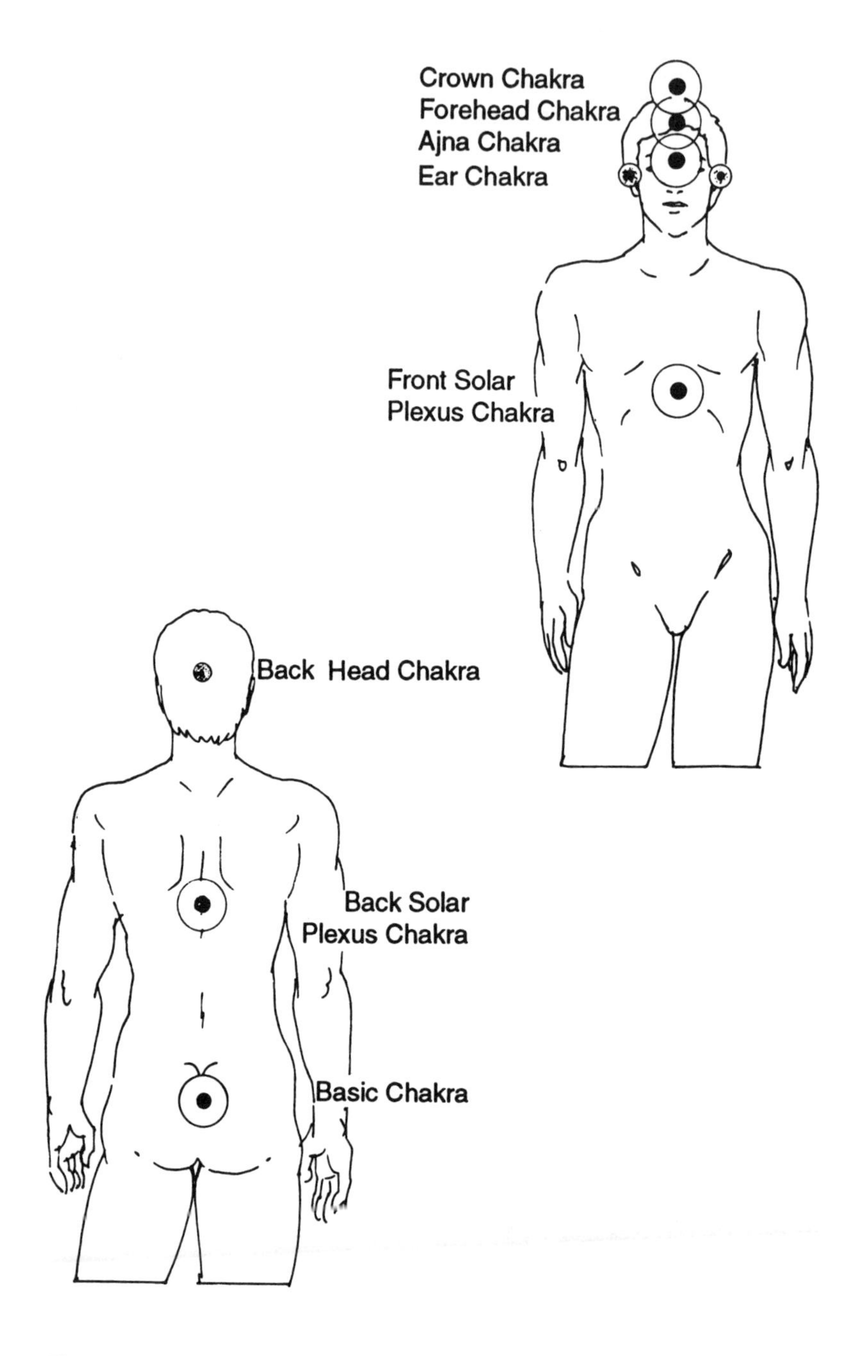

Figure 18. Treatment for visual and auditory hallucinations.

MEDITATION ON TWIN HEARTS

The practice of Meditation on Twin Hearts has cleansing effects on the energy body. It expels negative elementals and seals holes or cracks on the protective webs to a substantial degree. Therefore, it should be practiced daily by alcoholics, smokers, drug addicts, hallucinating patients and others. It is very important that the patients have a certain degree of intention to improve.

Healing Physical and Emotional Depression

The nature of the mind is such that it becomes that which it intensely thinks of.

—Swami Swananda

As you think, so you become.

—an esoteric maxim

Depressed patients are also very good in meditation. The only problem is that they meditate on negative things. The psychotherapist has to encourage patients to redirect their thoughts and feelings on positive things.

—C.K.S

DEPRESSION CAN be due to physical or psychological factors. During winter, a lot of older people experience depression because there is less vital energy in the air. This is an example of depression due to a physical factor. A person undergoing a lot of stress may, in the long run, become depressed and this is an example of depression due to psychological factors. A traumatic experience may destroy self-confidence that results in severe self-inhibition which may manifest as depression.

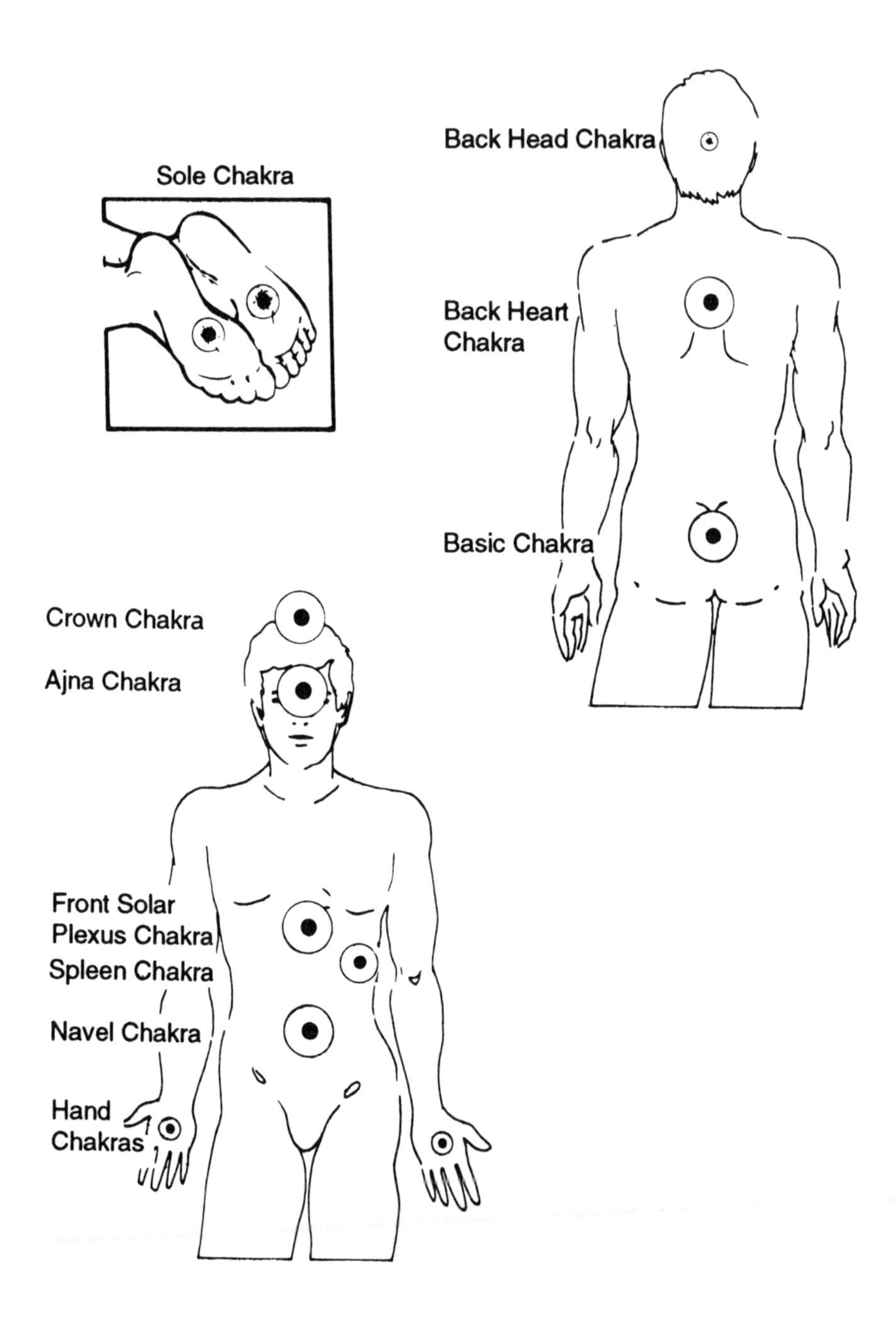

Figure 19. Treatment for depression.

Patients who are depressed have a depleted energy body. The basic chakra, navel chakra, spleen chakra, and the solar plexus chakra are depleted. See figure 19.

HEALING DEPRESSION BASED ON PHYSICAL FACTORS

1) Scan the major chakras and apply general sweeping thoroughly on the patient.

2) Apply localized sweeping and energizing on the hand chakras, sole chakras, basic chakra, navel chakra, spleen chakra, and solar plexus chakra with light-red pranic energy by using the basic/hand-chakra technique. Repeat the treatment twice a week or more depending upon the situation. For patients suffering from mild depression, the application of this healing technique will produce very good results after several treatments. In some cases, the effect is almost instantaneous.

Advanced pranic healers may use the master healing technique which will produce very fast results. But there are certain restrictions that you have to take into account. Please, consult my book, *Pranic Healing*.

DEPRESSION DUE TO PSYCHOLOGICAL FACTORS

The treatment for depression due to psychological factors is almost the same as the treatment due to physical factors. The stress energy—or traumatic energy—and the negative thoughts of fear, poor self-esteem, doubt, and pessimism have to be removed or cleansed from the solar plexus chakra, crown chakra, and the ajna chakra. The heart chakra has to be activated.

1) Apply the treatment for depression due to physical factors.

2) The heart chakra should be cleansed and energized through the back heart chakra with light-violet or electric violet pranic energy by using the crown/hand-chakra technique.

3) Apply localized cleansing and energizing on the entire head area–especially on the sides of the head, on the crown chakra, ajna chakra, and the solar plexus chakra with light-violet or electric violet pranic energy. Use the crown/hand-chakra technique with the intention to remove all the stress energy, traumatic energy, and all negative thoughts or thought entities from these chakras.

4) The solar plexus chakra in some cases is overactivated, but depleted. Inhibit the solar plexus chakra by energizing it with light blue pranic energy by using the throat/hand-chakra technique. In some cases, the patient is filled with anger and frustration, and is at times violent. The solar plexus chakra and the meng mein chakra are overactivated and have to be inhibited. Repeat the treatment several times a week.

The rate of improvement varies. With some patients, it may take only one session. With others, it may take several weeks or months for the patient to substantially improve, depending upon the severity of the depression and the skill of the healer.

COMPLEMENTARY SELF-PRANIC TREATMENT

1) Instruct the patient to do slow deep abdominal breathing and simultaneously to look at the problem or problems. The patient will be amazed that he or she is viewing the problem more objectively and from a more positive perspective. Instruct the patient to do a breathing meditation daily to help cope with the stress or emotional problem.

2) Instruct the patient to think and feel positively. This should become a habit. Unless he or she changes the way of thinking and feeling, there will only be limited progress.

3) Instruct the patient to create a positive self-image daily. This is done by externalizing and destroying negative thoughts and creating a positive thought-image of one's self. In other words, to regularly think and feel positively about one's self. Instruct the patient to visualize a positive image. Or make a positive affirmation about one's self. This has to be done daily. The visualization does not have to be clear. What is important is to have a clear intention. See chapter 3 for detailed instructions.

4) Instruct the patient to do the Meditation on Twin Hearts every day. It is an anti-depressant and has very beneficial effects.

5) The patient should do a lot of physical exercise. A change of environment will sometimes be very useful, since in some cases the patient's condition is aggravated by the negative attitudes of some of the members of the family. And at times, it may be necessary to give psychological counseling or pranic psychotherapy to some of them.

SEVERE DEPRESSION

For severe depression, the patient is very depleted. The inner aura is less than two inches and is quite gray. The chakras are quite small–only about two inches. With mild depression, the inner aura is slightly depleted or is not as dense as with ordinary healthy people.

1) If the patient is still capable of following instructions, then teach the patient to do deep pranic breathing for about ten minutes to energize himself or herself. Or let the patient lie down on the ground or floor and then apply general sweeping. The purpose is to let the patient absorb the ground pranic energy when general sweeping is applied. You may place a mat or a blanket

made of natural material on the ground or floor for the patient to lie down on.

2) Apply localized sweeping on the feet and hands. Energize the feet and hands with light-red pranic energy by using the basic hand-chakra technique. The sole chakras and the hand chakras draw in pranic energy from the surroundings, thereby, energizing the body. This is to make the work of the healer less taxing. You may rest for five to ten minutes to allow the patient's body to have enough time to energize itself.

3) Apply localized sweeping on the basic chakra, navel chakra, spleen chakra, and solar plexus chakra.

4) Energize the basic chakra, navel chakra, spleen chakra, and front solar plexus chakra with light-red pranic energy using the basic hand-chakra technique. Apply the treatment used for depression due to psychological factors. The treatment should be repeated every day if possible.

In treating very severely depressed patients, healers may feel their energy literally being sucked when energizing, since the chakras are starved for pranic energy. This is why it is important to follow the procedure properly. It is very helpful to give the patient five grams of Chinese or Korean ginseng capsules every day, especially just before treatment. Chinese or Korean ginseng contains a lot of synthetic ki which has activating and energizing effects. The dosage may be increased or decreased depending upon the age and the response of the patient.

SUICIDAL TENDENCIES

If the patient has suicidal tendencies, then the basic chakra is depleted and underactivated. The size is sometimes two inches in diameter or even smaller. The basic chakra is the center of self-preservation or the instinct of self-survival. This chakra has to be activated, while the solar plexus chakra is overactivated and has to be inhibited. Also the heart chakra has to be activated to produce inner peace. See figure 20.

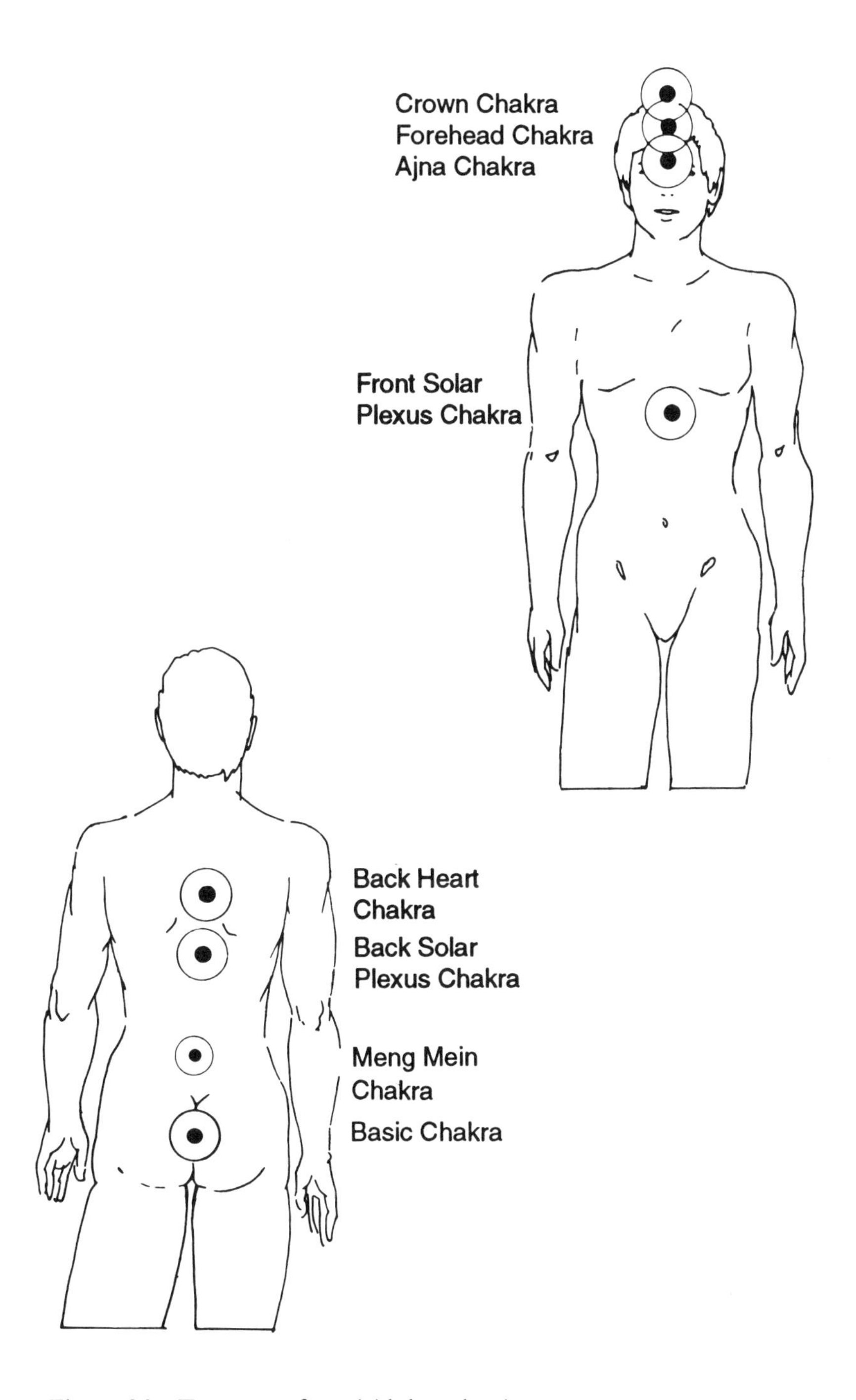

Figure 20. Treatment for suicidal tendencies.

1) Interview the patient.

2) Scan all the major chakras.

3) Apply general sweeping with light-violet or electric violet pranic energy by using the crown/hand-chakra technique.

4) Apply localized sweeping and energizing on the basic chakra with light-red pranic energy by using the basic hand-chakra technique. When energizing, will the basic chakra of the patient to become activated to about four inches. It is important to thoroughly energize the basic chakra. This is very critical.

5) Apply localized sweeping and energizing on the solar plexus chakra with light-violet or electric violet pranic energy by using the crown/hand-chakra technique. When applying sweeping on the solar plexus chakra, use your will to remove the negative thoughts and feelings lodged in it. Inhibit the solar plexus chakra with light-blue pranic energy by using the throat/hand-chakra technique. When energizing with light-blue pranic energy, you can also will the solar plexus chakra to normalize to three inches in diameter.

6) If the patient is violent, the meng mein chakra has to be inhibited with light-blue pranic energy by using the throat/hand-chakra technique.

7) Clean and energize the heart chakra through the back heart chakra with light-violet or electric violet pranic energy by using the crown/hand-chakra technique.

8) Clean and energize the crown chakra with light-violet or electric violet pranic energy by using the crown/hand-chakra technique. When applying localized sweeping, will to remove all negative thoughts and feelings lodged in the crown chakra.

9) Clean and energize the ajna chakra with light-violet or electric violet pranic energy by using the crown/hand-chakra technique. This increases the willpower of the patient.

10) Rescan the basic chakra and reenergize it with light-red pranic energy.

11) The patient should be given psychological counseling. The patient must be gradually and gently made aware that it is his or her negative attitude, thinking, and feeling that is creating or aggravating the problem.

12) Repeat the treatment at least twice a week, depending upon the severity of the ailment and the response of the patient. The patient should be closely monitored for the next few months. If possible, the relatives or close friends should be informed to keep a close watch on the patient.

The patient should be taught a breathing meditation. When the patient is normal enough to learn the Meditation on Twin Hearts, then he or she should be instructed to practice it every day. He or she should also be taught positive self-imaging.

TESTIMONIALS

This is the case of a male patient who was depressed and anxious because the company where he was working shut down. He decided to go into business, but this left him physically exhausted and drained him of his savings. He became very hopeless and worried about his future. He was prescribed a low dose of hypnotic medicine which he took for two nights. After three to four sessions, combining pranic healing with conventional psychotherapy, the patient's condition and outlook on life improved tremendously.

Healer:	Dr. Sonia L. Dy
Address:	Metropolitan Hospital Masangkay Street, Sta. Cruz Metro Manila
Occupation:	Psychiatrist and pranic psychotherapist
Case:	*Depression*

Morris complained of severe exhaustion, depression and intense anger caused primarily by his disappointment regarding a member of his family which left him with a feeling of being betrayed and let down. After only one healing session, he immediately felt relieved, as if something had been taken off his chest. Physically, he regained his strength, feeling the surging of renewed energy, and also felt emotionally recharged.

Healer: Dr. Sonia L. Dy
Address: Metropolitan Hospital
Masangkay Street, Sta. Cruz
Metro Manila
Occupation: Psychiatrist and pranic psychotherapist
Case: *Depression*

Marilyn, 15 years old, was referred to me by her grandmother because she was socially withdrawing. She refused to talk to her parents, confined herself to her room most of the time, quit school, and at one time, ran away from home. According to the grandmother, Marilyn was upset by the constant quarrelling of her parents and felt unloved and uncared for. This prompted her deep depression and anger. When she first came in for therapy, she appeared unkempt and refused to say even a word. On scanning, I found out that her navel, forehead, and ajna chakras were congested and overactivated, while her basic chakra was depleted. In the first pranic healing session, she claimed to have felt nothing. I saw her regularly twice a week applying a combination of conventional medication. Gradually, I saw her transformation. She exhibited enthusiasm to return to school, became communicative and cooperative to the therapists, her hygiene improved, and she was able to be more expressive of her feelings.

Healer: Dr. Sonia L. Dy
Address: Metropolitan Hospital
Masangkay Street, Sta. Cruz,
Metro Manila
Occupation: Psychiatrist and pranic psychotherapist
Case: *Depression*

6

Healing Violent and Paranoid Patients

In the inner world, like attracts like. Intense anger ruptures the protective webs. It attracts violent elementals, makes people insane and makes them do horrible things.

–C.K.S.

FOR EVERY violent patient, most major chakras have to be treated. The minor chakras in the arms and legs have to be treated also. The energy body of the patient is infested with violent negative elementals. The ajna chakra, the solar plexus chakra, the meng mein chakra, and the basic chakra are overactivated. These chakras have holes and have many negative elementals. The heart chakra and the forehead chakra are partially depleted and underactivated. The accumulated angry and suspicious thoughts and feelings, in the form of negative thought entities that are lodged on the solar plexus chakra, ajna chakra, and crown chakra, have to be cleansed. If the patient has been hearing strange ugly voices, then the ear chakras have to be treated. If the patient possesses incredible physical strength, the minor chakras in the arms and legs have to be treated. If the ailment is new, or has just developed recently, the treatment will be easy and will produce fast results. See figure 21 on page 74.

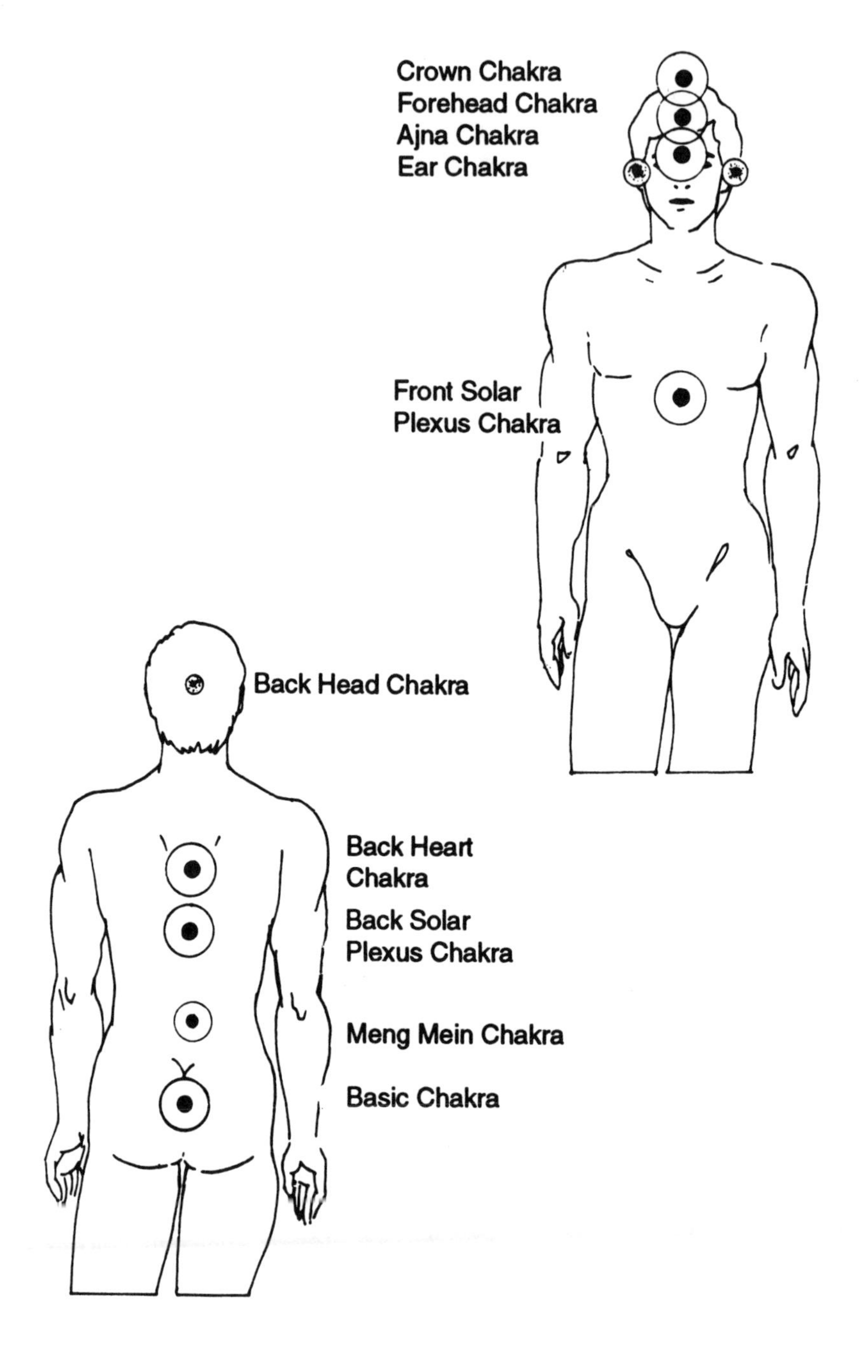

Figure 21. Treatment for violent and paranoid patients.

1) Scan the body thoroughly.

2) Apply general sweeping with light-violet or electric violet pranic energy by using the crown/hand-chakra technique.

3) Apply localized sweeping on the ajna chakra, solar plexus chakra, and basic chakra with light-violet or electric violet pranic energy by using the crown/hand-chakra technique. The healer must form an intention to remove the negative elementals and negative thoughts when localized sweeping is done. Energize these chakras with light-violet or electric violet pranic energy by using the crown/hand-chakra technique with the intention of disintegrating the remaining negative elementals and with the intention of sealing the cracks or holes on the protective webs. Cleansing and energizing have to be done alternately.

4) The ajna chakra, solar plexus chakra, meng mein chakra, and the basic chakra are overactivated and have to be inhibited. Apply localized sweeping on the meng mein chakra. Inhibit the solar plexus chakra, meng mein chakra and the ajna chakra by energizing them with blue pranic energy using the throat/hand-chakra technique. Visualize the blue pranic energy coming out of your hand and will the chakras to become smaller (about 2½ inches). If done properly, the patient will become calm. The person or persons restraining the patient will feel the patient has become "soft," and is no longer strong and violent.

5) Apply ordinary localized sweeping on the front heart chakra and energize the back heart chakra with light-violet or electric violet pranic energy by using the crown/hand-chakra technique with the intention of activating the heart chakra.

6) Apply localized sweeping on the crown chakra and the back head chakra using light-violet or electric violet pranic energy to remove the negative elementals and thought entities. Energize the crown chakra and back head chakra with light-violet pranic energy, with the intention of disintegrating the remaining negative elementals and thought entities, and sealing the holes or cracks.

7) The forehead chakra is depleted. Apply cleansing and energizing on it with light-violet or electric violet pranic energy by using the crown/hand-chakra technique.

8) If the patient has been hearing strange ugly voices, apply localized sweeping and energizing using violet or electric violet pranic energy on the ear chakras.

9) If the patient was quite violent and was very strong, clean and energize with light-violet or electric violet pranic energy the throat, secondary throat, navel, sex, armpit, elbow, hand, hip, knee and sole chakras.

10) For not-so-violent patients, repeat the treatment several times a week. For very violent patients, repeat the treatment several times a day for the next few days. Later adjust the frequency of the treatment upon the response of the patient.

TREATMENT FOR PARANOID PATIENTS

The treatment for paranoid patients is the same as the treatment for violent patients. The crown chakra, back head chakra, forehead chakra, ajna chakra, ear chakras, solar plexus chakra, meng mein chakra, and basic chakra are affected. Their protective webs have cracks and are filled with negative elementals, and/or filled with negative thought entities. Almost all of the mentioned chakras are cracked, or punctured, and are filled with negative elementals. The crown chakra, ajna chakra, and the solar plexus chakra are filled with accumulated negative thoughts and feelings or negative thought entities. The ajna chakra, solar plexus chakra, meng mein chakra, and the basic chakra are overactivated and have to be inhibited. The forehead chakra is depleted. Many violent patients are also paranoid.

RESTLESSNESS AND INSOMNIA

Many violent patients may have difficulty in sleeping and are very restless. They just cannot stay put or remain still. The basic chakra is overactivated. Its protective web has cracks or holes and is infested with negative elementals. See figure 22 on page 78.

1) Interview the patient.

2) Scan the major chakras.

3) Apply general sweeping with light-violet or electric violet pranic energy.

4) To remove the negative element and to seal the cracks or holes, just apply cleansing and energizing on the basic chakra with light-violet or electric violet pranic energy by using the crown/hand-chakra technique. Be sure to thoroughly energize the basic chakra.

5) Inhibit the basic chakra by energizing it with blue pranic energy by using the throat/hand-chakra technique. Will the basic chakra to reduce in size to 2½ inches.

6) The solar plexus chakra, the ajna chakra, and the crown chakra have to be cleansed and energized with light-violet or electric violet pranic energy by using the crown/hand-chakra technique. The solar plexus chakra has to be inhibited with light-blue pranic energy by using the throat/hand-chakra technique.

Treating the basic chakra is very important since the negative elementals embedded in the protective web of the basic chakra are the cause of restlessness and insomnia. Repeat the treatment several times a week. If the treatment is done properly, the patient should show improvement after several treatments. In order to produce rapid healing, one has to be very thorough.

The patient should be instructed to regulate his or her anger. Intense anger should be avoided since it ruptures the protective webs and attracts violent elementals to the angry person. The violent negative elementals are embedded on the protective webs and influence the angry person to do cruel and terrible things. In the "inner" world, like attracts like. This is why intense anger attracts violent negative elementals.

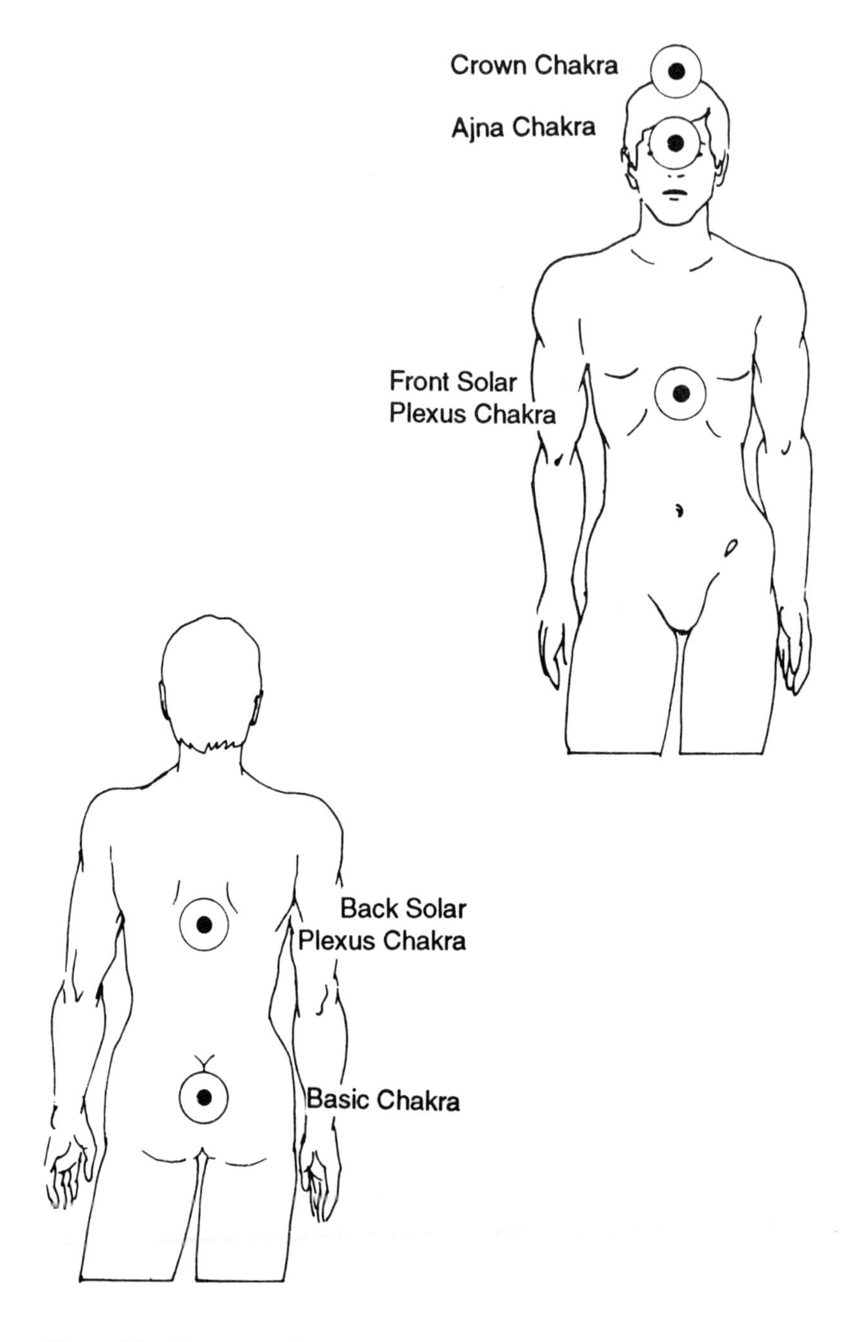

Figure 22. Treatment for restlessness and insomnia.

TEACHING THE PATIENT TO REGULATE ANGER

1) Teach the patient to do deep pranic breathing and instruct the patient to do it every day for at least ten minutes, and when irritated or angry.

2) Instruct the patient to meditate on the prayer of Saint Francis of Assisi for about ten minutes everyday. It has cleansing and calming effect.

3) Once the patient has gained sufficient calmness and the ability to concentrate; he or she should be taught the Meditation on Twin Hearts. Instruct the patient to do the Meditation on Twin Hearts every day for about ten minutes per session.

All of these practices will greatly accelerate the recovery of the patient.

Prayer of Saint Francis of Assisi

Lord, make me an instrument of Your peace.
Where there is hatred, let me sow love;
Where there is doubt, faith;
Where there is despair, hope;
Where there is darkness, light, and
Where there is sadness, joy.

O, Divine Master,

Grant that I may not so much
Seek to be consoled as to console;
To be understood as to understand;
To be loved as to love;
For it is in giving that we receive;
It is in pardoning that we are pardoned;
and it is in dying that we are born to eternal life.

TESTIMONIALS

For more than four years, I have been nervous, and fearful. At times, I felt that people were watching me. I was "jumpy." I cannot stay put in one place. I have to move around. Small things or irritations bother me. I have difficulty sleeping. I preferred to stay home and did not want to go out. I did not like to socialize. Recently, my arms were shaking uncontrollably even in public and I was quite embarrassed. According to the psychiatrist, the shaking was due to the reduction in dosage of the medicine I had been given.

After the first treatment, the shaking was reduced. I also felt more relaxed. I have been undergoing pranic psychotherapy three times a week for about two months. I feel good, at peace and not "jumpy." I am no longer restless. I am now sleeping soundly and I no longer feel like I am being watched. I feel a big improvement and I am now a new person physically and psychologically.

Date:	September 7, 1988
Patient:	B.M.
Address:	Withheld
Data:	21 years old, male
Case:	*Anxiety, Restlessness, Paranoia*

Gilda can be described as a shy person, a loner who claims she would really like to meet people but is hindered by an unusual fear of what other people may think of her. She consulted me because of insomnia and auditory hallucinations (as hearing voices of spiritual objects talking to her). Further, she claimed to possess supreme thought power and is thus able to command other people what to do. After two sessions, using pranic psychotherapy combined with a conventional psychiatric mode of treatment, her hallucinations together with all other complaints disappeared.

Date:	September 29, 1988
Healer:	Dr. Sonia L. Dy
Address:	Metropolitan Hospital Masangkay Street, Sta. Cruz Metro Manila
Occupation:	Psychiatrist and pranic psychotherapist
Case:	*Hallucination*

Samuel is a 25-year-old male patient who saw several psychiatrists for more than ten years. He was also on various medications but complained that his condition had not improved. His main problem stemmed from his unfavorable relationship with his father. He felt that he was always criticized and contradicted in all his ways. This had caused him intense anger which he claimed he could not control, and that when dreaming, he would notice that he had been cursing other people. According to relatives, this patient manifested a bad temper and was often verbally abusive of people–even of his elders. Using conventional psychiatric treatment combined with creative visualization, thought projection and pranic psychotherapy, the patient felt more relaxed and his anger was greatly reduced.

Date:	October 3, 1988
Healer:	Dr. Sonia L. Dy
Address:	Metropolitan Hospital Masangkay Street, Sta. Cruz Metro Manila
Occupation:	Psychiatrist and pranic psychotherapist
Case:	*Violent Tendency*

This is the case of a patient whom I saw three years ago. This time, she was admitted in a private hospital because of feelings of restlessness, of being overpowered by evil spirits, of electric sensations all over her body, and of suspiciousness that other people seemed to be against her. Upon probing, I found out that these symptoms were a result of various problems she encountered.

She had experienced trouble with her in-laws who could not seem to accept her as a daughter. This was further compounded by a husband who was not supportive of her emotionally, as well as financially, as the husband was out of work. An additional stress factor was work-related, as she felt she had to work hard to be able to provide for the family. After using pranic psychotherapy, the patient felt relaxed and immediately calmed down. Candidly, she claimed, "I feel as if I was made whole again." There were no signs of restlessness and her anxiety was tremendously reduced. She was discharged from the hospital within four days completely relieved of all symptoms.

Date:	October 5, 1988
Healer:	Dr. Sonia L. Dy
Address:	Metropolitan Hospital Metro Manila
Occupation:	Psychiatrist and pranic psychotherapist
Case:	*Paranoia*

Carol, a 27-year-old woman, had been suffering from a chronic case of schizophrenia for more than ten years. She complained of having auditory hallucinations with conflicting statements like "pangit ka" (you're ugly) and "maganda ka" (you're beautiful). She possessed a very poor self-image and kept on saying that she is "walang suwerte" (unlucky). She was being given neuroleptics or tranquilizers for her medication. During her check-ups, which were on and off, severe symptoms of hallucination were found present. On her last attack, she appeared violent and was desirous to hit some people. I decided to introduce pranic psychotherapy coupled with medicine, and in the first session, the patient said "nawala na ang malas" (the bad luck is gone). After regular sessions every two weeks, her suspiciousness disappeared and her hallucinations reached tolerable limits. She no longer paid attention to the voices she seemed to hear.

Date:	October 3, 1988
Healer:	Dr. Sonia L. Dy
Address:	Metropolitan Hospital Masangkay Street, Sta. Cruz Metro Manila
Occupation:	Psychiatrist and pranic psychotherapist
Case:	*Schizophrenia/Violent Tendencies*

In the later part of 1976, right after high school graduation, my son began acting strangely. An intelligent boy was now confused, moody, depressed and sometimes violent. He lost his senses. Smells, tastes, sounds and sights were distorted. There were moments when he heard strange voices, saw haunting things, his body odor was offensive. He suspected everyone was persecuting him. His memory was distorted, logic suspended, the mind sped and slowed without reason. He sometimes had delusions of personal power. He talked to himself; laughed and shouted at people. He was in continual depression, very restless, always walking, never resting. He lost his appetite, could not sleep. To relieve his tension he started smoking cigarettes and later smoked five packs a day. He withdrew from the world and stopped communicating with people. He had suicidal tendencies. The whole family lived in a world that sometimes became agonizing and even terrifying. He was diagnosed as schizophrenic.

For the next eleven years he was taken from one psychiatrist to another–from one hospital to another–and was treated with everything from tranquilizers to shock therapy. It was a heavy drain on our financial resources. We were on the verge of financial bankruptcy and cure was nowhere in sight. This thing is terrible. Because of intense caring for my son, I lost my physical energy and became ill myself.

Fortunately for me, I came across a book on pranic healing and immediately submitted myself for treatment. After several months of continuous treatment, I was almost completely healed of my heart and lung ailments. With this development, I decided to submit my son to pranic psychotherapy. After two months of treatments about three times a week, remarkable improvements were noticed:

1) His restlessness was reduced considerably and he is more relaxed now.

2) Smoking habits changed from five packs to two packs or less a day.

3) He communicates with people now.

4) His concentration has improved and now he plays the piano.

5) He now shaves his beard and observes cleanliness.

6) His posture has improved; he now looks straight and not down.

7) He is more obedient and easy to talk with.

8) Hallucinations and hearing of voices are gone.

9) He has regained his appetite.

10) He now has ambition.

For the first time in eleven years, these big improvements in his behavior have given me hope. My son is still getting treatments. With these I pray that pranic healing be made available to hundreds of thousands of patients suffering from severe psychological ailments who are suffering and who need help badly. This type of severe psychological ailment inflicts heavy damage on the family.

Date: November 25, 1988
Name: Edgardo B. Anacan
Address: 10 Liamson St., Midtown Sub.
San Roque, Marikina, Metro Manila
Case: *A son suffering from restlessness, depression, hallucination, strong violent and suicidal tendencies*

Healing by Prayer and Affirmation

O compassionate God, Thy Name is our healing; remembrance of Thee is our remedy!

–the Koran

What is not possible with man is possible with God.

–Bible

I AM NOT trying to convert anybody or make them become more religious. It has been observed that healing, when accompanied by prayer, is much more powerful and more effective. I prefer to use prayers that are simple and straight to the point. You may use these prayers or formulate your own.

Lord, thank you for Your Divine healing energy,
and for healing this patient.
In full faith! So be it!

In the name of God Almighty and All-merciful,
Unclean spirits be gone! So be it!
With thanks and in full faith!

In the name of God Almighty and All-merciful
you are clean, whole, and healed!
With thanks and in full faith!

Figure 23. Healing by prayer.

The prayer should be repeated several times while healing a patient. The treatment may have to be repeated several times a week. Healing by prayer is very potent and very effective. For very powerful healers, it is very important not to overenergize the patient. As you become more excited and more powerful, do not use too much will when healing because the patient may get worse. See figure 23.

SELF-HEALING AFFIRMATION

God is almighty, God is merciful, He is healing me of (specify the ailment/s). With thanks and in full faith! So be it.

1) Repeat this prayer for about 15 minutes with full concentration, humility, reverence, and faith.

2) When done properly, it will bring rapid relief for simple ailments.

3) For people suffering from severe ailments, repeat this prayer for about 15 minutes twice daily, for as long as necessary, even if it takes several months or years.

4) Self-healing affirmation is complementary to the Mediation on Twin Hearts. For those suffering from severe ailments, do the Meditation on Twin Hearts; after that, do the self-healing affirmation. By combining the two, the rate of healing will be much faster.

If symptoms persist or if the ailment is severe, please consult a physician and a pranic healer.

DIVINE SELF

> *What? know ye not that your body is the temple of the Holy Ghost which is in you, which ye have of God?*
>
> –I Corinthians: 6:19

> *For behold, the kingdom of God is within you!*
>
> –Luke 17:21

> *So God created man in his own image.*
>
> –Genesis 1:27

> *For in him we live, and move, and have our being.*
>
> –Acts 17:28

Spirit soul is different from this body in that its nature is immutable, indestructible and eternal.

–Bhagavad Gita

Buddha-nature (or the divine self) exists in everyone no matter how deeply it may be covered over by greed, anger and foolishness, or buried by their own deeds and retribution; and when all defilements are removed, sooner or later, it will reappear.

–Wisdom of the Buddha

The reader must realize by now that he or she is not the body nor the emotions nor the thoughts and that all of these statements simply mean that you are the divine self within your body, and that this divine self is part of God. In other words, you are a divine being. There is a divine flame or a godhead within you. You can use the power of God manifesting through your divine self to heal yourself of physical and psychological ailments. This can be done by repeating this affirmation several minutes every day or for as long as necessary.

I am not the body, nor the emotion, nor the thought.
I am a divine being!
I am That I am!
I am clean, whole, and healed.
With thanks. So be it!

To free yourself from negative elementals, you can use this affirmation:

I am a divine being.
I am That I am.
By the power of the godhead within me,
I command all of you to leave now!

or

By the power of God manifesting through my divine self!
I command you to go away, now!
In full faith! So be it!

Repeat this affirmation as many times as necessary.

HEALING BY COMMAND

Patients can be cleansed of negative elementals by just commanding them to leave and not to return. This is applicable to experienced healers whose *antakharana* or spiritual cord is relatively well-developed.

1) Concentrate on the crown chakra.
2) Mentally or verbally command:

By the Power of God
manifesting through
my divine self!
Negative elementals, be gone!
Do not return!

or

Unclean spirits, be gone!
Never return!

The command can be given once or several times.

Apply pranic psychotherapy to seal the protective webs and to normalize the chakras. The treatment has to be repeated for as long as necessary.

CHAKRAL AND AURIC SHIELDS

Since there is a tendency for the patient to again rupture the protective webs and attract negative elementals, it is advisable to create chakral shields for the affected chakras and to create auric shields to prevent negative elementals from psychically reinfecting the patients again. To create chakral shields, do the following:

1) Project electric violet prana by using the crown/hand-chakra technique on the affected chakra or chakras.

2) Visualize an electric violet ball of light shielding the chakra/s and the protective web.

3) Program the shields by mentally saying:

> *You are shielded from all negative elementals.*
> *Remain for a duration of three days.*
> *So be it!*

4) Create chakral shields on the affected chakras, especially, the front and back solar plexus, ajna, crown and basic chakras. Repeat the creation of the chakral shields after two days.

To create Auric Shields:

1) Concentrate on your crown chakra.

2) Visualize a mercury lamp.

3) Visualize the patient as very small and inside the mercury lamp.

4) Visualize the outer shell of the mercury lamp as brilliant electric violet light.

5) Program the shields by mentally saying:

> *You are shielded from all negative elementals.*
> *Remain for a duration of three days.*
> *So be it!*

6) Repeat the creation of the auric shields after two days.

It is very important that programming of the shield should be made properly. The chakral and the auric shields are used only to prevent the negative elementals from entering the aura and the chakras. It should not be used to prevent negative emotions and thoughts from going out of the chakras and the outer aura. Otherwise, the patient will become more imbalanced.

The creation of chakral and auric shields should preferably be done by experienced pranic healers or pranic psychotherapists. The creation of the chakral and the auric shields is very important. It creates a clean or sterile psychic internal environment for the patient. This is similar to orthodox medicine. Patients are kept in a clean or sterile room to minimize possible bacterial or viral infection.

For proficient psychotherapists, it is a must to create chakral and auric shields for patients who are violent, oversuspicious, hallucinating, or addicted to drugs. Psychological patients with chakral and auric shields will get well much faster compared to patients with no chakral and auric shields. If done properly, the result would be quite amazing, and the rate of healing will be much faster by several months.

PSYCHOLOGICALLY RETARDED PATIENTS

Psychologically retarded patients are very difficult to heal. Small noticeable improvements may take months. The treatment will have to be continued for years. With psychologically retarded patients, the crown chakra, forehead chakra, ajna chakra, back head chakra, throat chakra, and the spine are affected. The eyes and ears may also be affected. The basic and the sex chakras are partially depleted and have to be treated.

1) Interview the parents or guardian.

2) Scan the entire body, especially the major chakras, the eyes and ears, and the spine.

3) Apply general sweeping.

4) Apply localized sweeping and energizing on the entire brain, crown chakra, forehead chakra, ajna chakra, back head chakra, and the spine with light-violet or electric violet pranic energy by using the crown/hand-chakra technique.

5) Apply localized sweeping and energizing on the ears with light-violet or electric violet pranic energy by using the crown/hand-chakra technique.

6) Clean the eyes thoroughly. Energize the ajna chakra and the back head chakra with light-violet or electric violet pranic energy by using the crown/hand-chakra technique.

7) Clean and energize the basic chakra and the sex chakra with light-red pranic energy by using the basic/hand-chakra technique. This is very important because a portion of the pranic energy from the basic chakra and sex chakra are automatically transmuted to higher forms of pranic energy to be used by the upper chakras. This is needed for the proper functioning of the upper chakras.

8) Repeat the treatment two to three times a week.

THE CHARACTER OF AN UNBORN BABY AFFECTED BY THE FEELINGS AND THOUGHTS OF ITS PREGNANT MOTHER

The predominating thoughts and feelings of a pregnant woman are lodged in some of the major chakras of the unborn baby. Therefore, they will affect the character of the unborn baby. In order to produce better babies, it is very important for pregnant women to see and hear things that are beautiful, inspiring, and strong. Their feelings and thoughts should be harmonious, progressive, and positive. Anger, pessimism, hopelessness, injurious words, negative feelings, and negative thoughts should be avoided.

Can children who have been polluted, when still in the womb, by the negative thoughts and feelings of the pregnant mothers be healed? The answer is yes. The usual affected major chakras are the solar plexus chakra, ajna chakra, the crown chakra, and the basic chakra. They can be cleansed by applying localized sweeping on these chakras with light-violet or electric violet pranic energy.

PREVENTION OF PSYCHOLOGICAL AILMENTS

1) Learn to relax emotionally. This is done by doing slow deep abdominal breathing daily. Do this especially if there is a lot of work or family tension.

2) As much as possible, avoid negative emotions and thoughts. Think, feel, and act positively.

3) Avoid intense anger or hatred. These intense negative emotions rupture the protective webs, attracting and enabling foreign intruders or negative elementals to overwhelm the person. This can make the person temporarily "insane" or "possessed" and he or she can do very bad things.

4) Avoid hallucinogenic drugs since they burn up some of the protective webs, thereby opening the users to negative elementals or influences which are usually beyond their control. Similarly, too much alcohol should be avoided because of its negative physical and psychological effects.

5) Do the Meditation on Twin Hearts every day. It cleanses and transmutes lower emotions to higher emotions. It has very soothing and peaceful effect on the meditator.

6) Do regular physical exercises, or dance regularly, since it releases pent-up negative emotions. One should let go of oneself when doing the physical exercises or when dancing. Otherwise, it will defeat its purpose.

7) If you have problem children, avoid negative feelings, thoughts, and words about them, since this would only make them worse. Avoid fighting in front of your children, since the anger and hatred will contaminate them and make them psychologically imbalanced.

HEALTH PROBLEMS ENCOUNTERED BY PSYCHOTHERAPISTS

1) Depression is *commonly* experienced by psychotherapists. This is due to the involuntary transference of pranic energy from the psychotherapist to the depressed patient, since energy flows from high energy density to low energy density, and also due to contamination from the diseased energy of the patients.

2) Psychotherapists may become erratic and at times even violent to a certain degree. When psychotherapists listen to the problems of their patients, they are actually being used as psychic garbage cans. Some of the psychic garbage is disintegrated or transmuted by the body's natural defense mechanism. Some is *retained*. This accumulation of psychic garbage from patients will tend to make psychotherapists psychologically erratic. This can be minimized by doing the Meditation on Twin Hearts after healing or counseling patients, by undergoing pranic treatment at least once a week, and by having regular vacations.

3) Sometimes psychotherapists may experience difficulty breathing and some sort of heaviness on the solar plexus area. The solar plexus chakra is congested due to contamination and the accumulation of psychological diseased energy. This can be corrected by asking a pranic healer to clean and energize the solar plexus chakra.

4) Psychotherapists may experience chest pain and numbness in the shoulder and arm. The heart chakra is overactivated, but depleted. The work of psychotherapists involves a lot of "calm" or

"detached" compassion toward patients. This involves the use of "heart energy" which has soothing and healing effects on patients. As a result, the heart chakra is overused and becomes depleted. The solution is to have regular pranic treatment and have a vacation. Healers may use the heart/hand-chakra technique to project heart energy to the patient. I do not encourage the frequent use of this technique because if this technique is not properly done, or is overused, the healers will experience chest pain and develop heart ailments.

It is not advisable for psychotherapists to form a protective shell around themselves. When patients talk to psychotherapists, they release some of their pent-up negative emotions to psychotherapists. The released negative emotions will hit the protective shell and will bounce back to the patients with even greater strength, making the patients worse. In esoteric parlance, this is called the boomerang effect.

When somebody sends you negative thoughts and you do not respond, the negative energy bounces back to the sender. The negative thought, in the process of returning, attracts similar negative energy and thoughts. By the time it boomerangs back to the sender, its strength has already increased many times.

Psychotherapists should do a lot of physical exercise and the Meditation on Twin Hearts to decontaminate themselves. The Meditation on Twin Hearts has expelling and transmuting effects. It also enhances your healing skills.

Go and heal the sick!

–Matthew 10:8

Go and do your duty:
show kindness to thy brothers
and free them from suffering.

–Lord Buddha

Commentary

by Sr. Mary Fidelis Estrada, R.A.[1]

I AM MOST grateful for this opportunity to go and tell others how my involvement in Pranic Healing continues to deepen and energize my experience of Jesus' promise, "I am come that they might have life, and that they might have it more abundantly" (John 10:10). Yes, being fulfilled before my very eyes, my heart-felt appreciation is anchored in personal conviction born out of Jesus' own words:

> *Verily, verily, I say unto you, He that believeth in me, the works that I do shall he do also; and greater works than these shall he do; because I go unto my Father.*
>
> –John 14:12

> *Jesus answered and said unto them, Go and shew John again those things which ye do hear and see. The blind receive their sight, and the lame walk, the lepers are cleansed, and the deaf hear, the dead are raised up, and the poor have the gospel*

---

[1] Sr. Mary Fidelis Estrada is a nun in the Catholic Church. She received her R. A. from Assumption College, San Lorenzo Village, Makati, Metro Manila, January, 1989.

preached to them. And blessed is he, whosoever shall not be offended in me.

–Matthew 11:4–6

The whole of Jesus' life on Earth was a persistent and faithful invitation to open ourselves more and more completely to the Father's love even while "in transit" on this earthly sojourn . . . to our Father Who loves us unto Life. His Life! Physical, emotional and spiritual ailments restrict and even block completely the free flow of God's Life in us. Furthermore, what we are experiencing on the emotional and spiritual levels influences us considerably, to the point of affecting our physical well-being.

Anyone versed in Scriptures will have noted that Jesus' physical healings were most often accompanied, if not prefaced, by inner healing.

Prior to my involvement in Pranic Healing, I devoted much time to praying with others for personal, as well as communal, healing. The end of the '60s, right up to August, 1989, saw me involved in the Catholic Charismatic Renewal, both here and in East Africa. (I served in Kenya from 1980 to 1988.)

Very often, I found myself with men and women, young and old, crying out for healing, for wholeness, for greater purpose in life. Each time, I felt greatly privileged to witness and experience the Lord's healing and reconciling presence flow out to these brothers and sisters through me. I know what it feels like to serve as a channel of the Father's love and compassion, leaving one feeling "very small" and humble, yet filled with awe and wonder!

A few hours after I came home from Africa in August, 1988, a number of my sisters accompanied their "welcome back!" with "you must attend the pranic healing workshop that will be held at our place next week!" To my very naive, "what is pranic healing?" my companions echoed with a smile: "You still don't know about it, but all these years, you've actually been doing it in bits and pieces!"

Pranic healing and pranic psychotherapy have led me to see and feel and touch so much more of what I have always believed–that every person is made in the image and likeness of God. His life flowing through us invites all those who believe in Him to do the same works that He did, and even greater ones, just as He promised!

And because it is often the economically deprived and the single-hearted (i.e., the pure of heart) who open themselves most simply and readily to God's saving action communicated through pranic healing and pranic psychotherapy, the good news of fuller, more abundant life and well-being continues to be proclaimed to them!

Far from unsettling or shaking my faith, pranic healing and pranic psychotherapy have led me to a deeper understanding and appreciation of the Scriptures, especially of Jesus, the Healer par excellence! These continue to add to my experience of the power of Love: "That Christ may dwell in your hearts by faith; that ye, being rooted and grounded in love, may be able to comprehend with all saints what is the breadth, and length, and depth, and height; And know the love of Christ, which passeth knowledge, that ye might be filled with all the fulness of God" (Ephesians 3:17–19).

Hand-in-hand with the joy of discovering and using pranic healing and pranic psychotherapy has been the realization that friends who have not really bothered to find out what these are all about, or who have approached it with preconceived ideas, have judged us who pray for healing this way as not Catholic. But the experience of this wisdom described in the Scriptures as not the wisdom of this age but God's wisdom: mysterious, hidden wisdom (see I Corinthians 2:6–7) of which is written that the eyes have not seen nor ears heard, nor has it entered the hearts of men, the rewards that God has reserved for those who love and fear Him (see I Corinthians 2:9), taking flesh every day in our very midst far outweighs any label!

A word about my teacher in the science and art of pranic healing and pranic psychotherapy, Master Choa Kok Sui: "By their fruits, you shall know them," says Jesus. "But the fruit of the Spirit is love, joy, peace, patient endurance, kindness, generosity, faith, mildness and self-control" (Gal. 5:22–23). I know from experience that Master Choa continues to plant seeds of kindness, peace, love, generosity, gentleness, faith and unity in my life and in the lives of countless others! Such is his harvest, too. And deep down in my heart, I know only a man of God can sow and harvest thus! I consider myself truly blessed to have a teacher and a friend in Master Choa! My response to the Lord's "Go to my brothers and tell them. . . ."

> *. . . we have heard it; we have seen it with our own eyes; we have looked upon it and felt it with our own hands; and it is of this we tell. Our theme is the word of life. . . . What we have seen and heard we declare to you, so that you and we together may share in a common life . . .*
>
> –Letters: I John 1:1,3

Yes, to you who read this personal witness and appreciation, and to those whom you will talk to about what I have experienced of this sign of the presence of God's reign in our midst today–pranic healing and psychotherapy–I entrust this Gift of Love that the Father has blessed me with. This very same Gift, He offers you, too!

APPENDIX A

Basic Techniques in Elementary and Intermediate Pranic Healing

THE INFORMATION that follows has been extracted from *Pranic Healing* for those readers who have no experience with using this method. You should become familiar with all the techniques and practices discussed in *Pranic Healing* before trying to use them to help people with emotional problems.

There are basic techniques you will need to learn in order to work with pranic healing. They are:

1) Sensitizing the hands;

2) Scanning the inner aura;

3) Sweeping or cleansing (general and localized);

4) Energizing with prana (Hand Chakras Technique) to draw in prana and to project prana;

5) Stabilizing the projected prana.

All these techniques have been tried and tested. Most of you will be able to produce positive results in just a few sessions by properly following the instructions. It is very important to maintain an open mind and to be persevering. Practice immediately what you have read and try the techniques for at least four sessions.

SENSITIZING THE HANDS

Since it would take a considerable amount of time to develop the auric sight, you should try to sensitize your hands in order to feel the bioplasmic energy field or the inner aura in order to determine which areas of the patient's bioplasmic body are depleted or congested.

1) Place your hands about three inches apart facing each other. Do not tense, just relax. (See figure 1.)

2) Concentrate on feeling the center of your palms and simultaneously be aware of your entire hand for about five to ten minutes. At the same time, inhale and exhale slowly and rhyth-

Figure 1. Sensitizing the hands.

mically. Concentration is facilitated by pressing the centers of your palms with your thumbs before starting. It is by concentrating at the center of the palms that the hand chakras are activated, thereby sensitizing the hands or enabling the hands to feel subtle energy or matter.

Eighty to ninety percent of you will be able to feel a tingling sensation, heat, pressure or rhythmic pulsation between the palms on the first try. It is important to feel the pressure or the rhythmic pulsation.

3) Proceed immediately to scanning after sensitizing your hands.

4) Practice sensitizing your hands for at least two weeks. Your hands should be more or less permanently sensitized after two weeks of practice.

5) Do not be discouraged if you do not feel anything on the first try. Continue your practice; you should be able to feel these subtle sensations on the third or fourth session. It is very important to keep an open mind and to concentrate properly.

SCANNING

In scanning, it is helpful (but not really necessary) to first learn how to feel the size and shape of the outer and health auras before scanning the inner aura. This is to make your hands more sensitive since both the outer and health auras are subtler than the inner aura and also to prove to yourself the existence of the outer and health auras. In healing, we are primarily interested in scanning the inner aura. It is in scanning the inner aura that the trouble spots can be located.

When scanning with your hands, always concentrate at the center of your palms. It is by concentrating at the center of your palms that the hand chakras remain or are further activated; thereby making the hands sensitive to subtle energy or matter. Without doing this you will have difficulty in scanning.

SCANNING THE INNER AURA

1) Proceed to feel the inner aura with one or both hands. Move your hands slowly and slightly back and forth to feel the inner aura. The inner aura is usually about five inches in thickness. Concentrate at the center of your palms when scanning. It is by concentrating at the center of the palms that your hand chakras remain or are further activated; thereby making your hands sensitive to subtle energy or matter.

2) Scan your subject from head to foot and from front to back. Scan the left part and right part. For example, scan the left and right ears, or scan the right and left lungs. When the inner aura of the right part and left part of the body are scanned, they should have about the same thickness. If one part is bigger or smaller than the other part, then there is something wrong with it. For instance, the ears of a patient were scanned and it was found out that the inner aura of the left ear was about five inches thick, while the inner aura of the right ear was only about two inches thick. The patient, when questioned, revealed that the right ear has been partially deaf for the past seventeen years.

3) Special attention should be given to the spine, to the vital organs, and to the major chakras. In many cases, a portion of the spine is usually either congested or depleted even if the patient does not complain about back problem.

4) In scanning the throat area, the chin should be raised upward in order to get accurate scanning. The inner aura of the chin tends to interfere or camouflage the actual condition of the throat.

5) Scanning of the lungs should be done at the back and at the sides rather than the front in order to get accurate results. The nipples have two mini chakras that tend to interfere in the proper scanning of the lungs. A more advanced technique is to scan the lungs at the front, at the back and at the sides by using two fingers, instead of using the entire hand.

6) Special attention should be given to the solar plexus since many diseases of emotional origin negatively affect the solar plexus chakra.

SWEEPING

Sweeping is generally a cleansing technique. It can also be used for energizing and distributing excess prana. When cleansing is done on the whole bioplasmic body, it is called *general sweeping*. Cleansing done on specific parts of the body is called *localized sweeping*.

The hands are used in sweeping. There are two hand positions: the *cupped-hand position* and the *spread-finger position*. These two hand positions are used alternately. The cupped-hand position is more effective in removing the diseased bioplasmic matter and the spread-finger position is more effective in combing and disentangling the health rays. General sweeping has been called aura cleansing or combing by some esoteric students.

Sweeping produces the following results:

1) It removes congested and diseased bioplasmic matter. Blocked meridians or bioplasmic channels are cleansed and unclogged. This allows prana from other parts of the body to flow to the affected part, facilitating the healing process.

2) Expelling of toxins, wastes, germs, and dirty bioplasmic matter is greatly facilitated by disentangling and partially strengthening the health rays. The health rays are further strengthened by energizing the whole body with prana.

3) By disentangling and strengthening the health rays, the health aura, which acts as a protective shield, is normalized. This increases one's resistance against infection.

4) Sweeping automatically seals holes in the outer aura through which prana leaks out. Without sealing the holes in the outer

aura, the healing process is very slow even if the patient is energized with prana because prana would just simply leak out. This is one of the contributing factors in regression. The disease sometimes comes back in a few minutes or hours after the patient has been healed when this sealing is not done.

5) Absorption of prana by the patient is greatly facilitated after sweeping or cleansing.

6) Sweeping is also used to distribute excess prana in a treated area to other parts of the body after it has been energized to prevent possible congestion.

7) Sweeping is used to energize by directing excess prana from the surrounding areas of the body or from a chakra or chakras to the affected part that is low in prana. For instance, a mild form of arthritis of the fingers was cured in minutes just by cleansing the fingers and sweeping or directing the excess prana from the hand chakra to the affected fingers.

8) Radical reaction is reduced or avoided by simply sweeping the patient thoroughly.

Sweeping is a very important pranic healing technique and it is very easy to learn. It cleanses, strengthens, and greatly facilitates the healing process. Many simple illnesses can be healed just by sweeping.

GENERAL SWEEPING EXERCISE

General sweeping is done with a series of *downward sweeping movements* only. In downward sweeping, you start from the head and work down to the feet. Upward sweeping movements are not used in cleansing but are used only to reawaken patients who may have fallen asleep or who may have become slightly drowsy. In upward sweeping, you start from the feet and work up to the head. See figure 2.

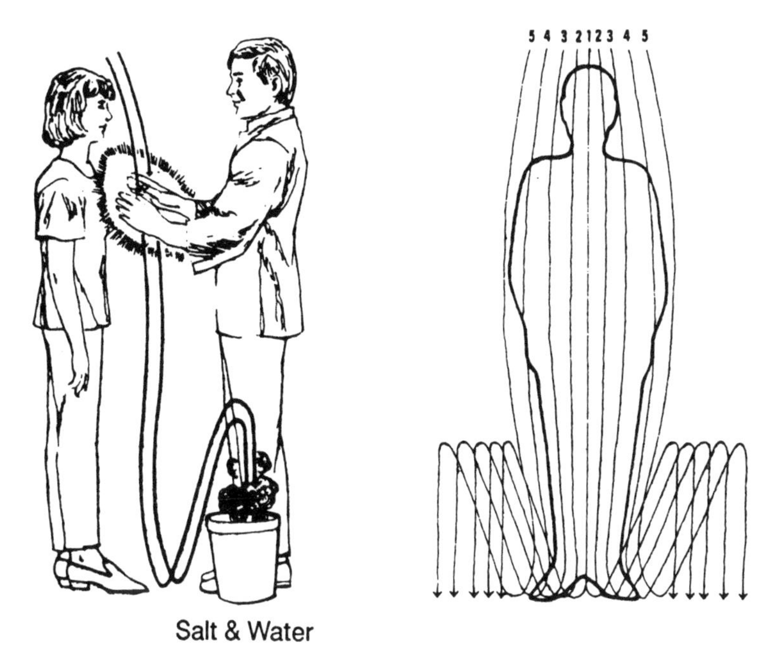

Figure 2. General sweeping. By cleansing or removing the diseased energy, circulation of vital energy, or prana, is enhanced, thereby increasing the rate of healing.

1) Cup your hands and place them six inches above the head of the patient. Do not unnecessarily touch the patient. Maintain a distance of about two inches between the patient's body and your hands.

2) With your hands still cupped, sweep your hands slowly downward from the head to the feet following line #1 as shown in figure 2. Slightly raise your hands and strongly flick them downward to throw away the dirty diseased bioplasmic matter. This is very important to avoid recontaminating the patient with the diseased bioplasmic matter; and also to avoid contaminating yourself, which would result not only as pain in your fingers, hands, and palms, but may result in the weakening of your body and/or illness similar to that of the patient.

3) Repeat the process discussed in procedure 2 (above) with spread-finger position instead of the cupped-hand position. This is to disentangle and strengthen the health rays. This is called combing.

4) Repeat the whole process in procedures 2 and 3 on lines 2, 3, 4, and 5 as shown in figure 2.

5) Apply downward sweeping on the back of the patient by following procedures 2, 3, and 4.

6) It is very important to concentrate and to form an intention to remove the diseased bioplasmic matter. Without this, the sweeping process becomes less effective and more time-consuming. It is the intention or the application of the will with the aid of the hands that the diseased bioplasmic matter is thoroughly and quickly removed. With regular practice, you can apply sweeping with great ease and with minimum effort.

7) After the downward sweeping, some patients may become sleepy. You may apply a few upward sweeping movements to reawaken or make the patient more alert. There is no need to flick your hands after the upward sweeping. Upward sweeping is not a cleansing technique, but a technique to reawaken the patient. It should be applied only after the patient has been relatively cleansed. Warning: Upward sweeping before applying the downward sweeping may result in the diseased bioplasmic matter going to or getting stuck in the head area, which may have negative physical effects.

LOCALIZED SWEEPING EXERCISE

1) Place your hand or hands above the affected area and slowly sweep away the diseased bioplasmic matter. This is just like cleaning a dirty object with your hand. (See figure 3.)

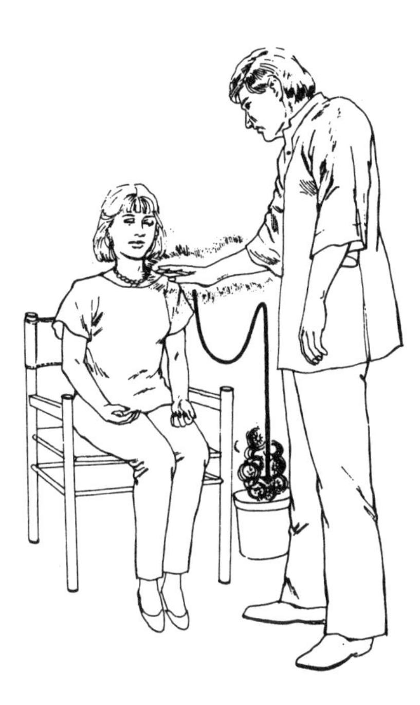

Figure 3. Localized sweeping. The rate of healing is increased by cleansing or removing the diseased energy from the affected part.

2) Strongly flick your hand to throw away the dirty bioplasmic matter.

3) The sweeping movements can be done in any direction: vertically, horizontally, diagonally or in L-shape.

Sweeping is very easy and can be learned almost immediately by most people. Sometimes in localized sweeping, the diseased bioplasmic matter is transferred from the affected part to another part of the body. For instance, one practitioner was sweeping away the congested bioplasmic matter at the back of the head of a patient, and part of it was transferred to the neck and shoulder areas. This caused the pain at the back of the head to partially move to the neck and shoulder areas. Should you encounter a similar situation, just simply apply localized sweeping on the new affected area.

How many times should general sweeping and localized sweeping be applied on a patient? The answer is as many times as required. There is no fixed number of times. Usually, I apply general sweeping once or twice and localized sweeping four or five times. However, in the case of a dog dying due to an accidental intake of slow acting poison, it was necessary to apply general sweeping and localized sweeping twenty to thirty times per session since after each sweeping and partially removing the darkish grey bioplasmic matter from the dog, the darkish grey matter would reappear after a few seconds and later after a few minutes. Sweeping and energizing was applied alternately. This whole process was repeated once every two hours and three times the first day. Healing was continued for the next few days. After about two weeks the dog became relatively active and healthy.

In case of poisoning, do not try to use only pranic healing. Get proper medical treatment and apply pranic healing to strengthen and facilitate the healing process. As stated earlier, a disease or illness could be caused by internal and/or external factors. If the cause is malnutrition, obviously enough nourishing food or nutritional supplements should be taken by the patient. Since chemical poison is a physical or external factor, then one should definitely use a physical or chemical form of treatment. Pranic healing should also be used to minimize the damage done to the body and to greatly facilitate the healing process.

In the case of the dying dog, the poison was already fully assimilated into its system and the veterinarian did not have any antidote; therefore, pranic healing was used alone because it was the only solution available at that time.

Although there are probably some great yogi, shamans or healers who can neutralize poison in their own bodies or the body of another person, who among us belongs to this caliber? In pranic healing, as well as in other field of activities, one should be fully aware of one's capabilities and limitations and should use sound judgment or common sense in making decisions.

ENERGIZING WITH PRANA HAND CHAKRA TECHNIQUE

When projecting prana to the patient's bioplasmic body, you should simultaneously draw in air prana or air vitality globule from the surroundings. This prevents draining or exhausting yourself and becoming susceptible to infection and diseases.

There are many ways of drawing in prana and projecting prana; one of the safest and easiest ways is through the hand chakras. One of the hand chakras is used to draw in air prana and the other to project prana or vital energy to the patient. Both left and right hand chakras can either predominantly draw in or project prana. The hand chakra is alternately drawing in and projecting prana at a rapid rate. Whether it predominantly draws in prana or predominantly projects prana is a matter of intention or willing. You can use either the right hand chakra to project prana and the left hand chakra to draw in prana, or vice versa. This is a matter of personal preference. With right-handed people, it is easier to draw in prana using the left hand chakra and project prana with the right hand chakra, and vice versa for left-handed people. See figure 4 on page 112.

Prana is drawn in through one of the hand chakras and projected through the other hand chakra. Attention or concentration should be focused on the hand chakras (on the centers of the palms) and on the part to be treated, with more emphasis on the hand chakras. Focusing too much on the part being treated is a mistake commonly made by beginners. This tends to reduce the flow of prana coming in and going out.

Use the following procedure:

1) Press the center of your palms with your thumb to facilitate your concentration.

2) Concentrate or focus your attention at the center of the palm that will be used for drawing in pranic energy for about ten to fifteen seconds. This is to partially activate the hand chakra, en-

Figure 4 Energizing with prana using the Hand Chakra Technique. A and B) Press the center of your palms with your thumb to facilitate your concentration; C) concentrate at the center of the palm that will be used for drawing in pranic energy for about 15 seconds; D) to energize, place the other hand near the affected part and concentrate simultaneously at the center of each palm.

hancing its ability to draw in pranic energy. If you intend to draw in pranic energy through your left hand, then concentrate at its center.

3) Place the other hand near the affected part and concentrate simultaneously at the centers of both hands. If you intend to project with your right hand chakra, then place your right hand near the affected part. Maintain a distance of about three to four inches away from the patient. Continue concentrating or focusing your attention at the centers of your palms until the patient is sufficiently energized. For simple cases, this may take about five to fifteen minutes for beginners.

4) When energizing or projecting prana, you must will or form an initial intention directing the projected prana to go to the affected chakra and then to the affected part. It is a critical factor that the projected prana be directed to the affected part; this will produce a much faster rate of relief and healing. Just energizing the affected chakra without willing or directing the pranic energy to go to the affected part would result in a slower distribution of prana or vital energy from the treated chakra to the affected part; thereby producing a much slower rate of relief and healing.

5) The left and right armpits should be slightly opened to allow easier flow of prana from one hand chakra to the other hand chakra.

6) There should be an initial expectation or intention to draw in prana from one hand chakra to the affected part and to project prana from the other hand chakra. Once the initial intention or expectation has been formed, there is no need to further consciously expect or will to project. The initial expectation and concentration on the two hand chakras causes prana to be automatically drawn in through one of the hand chakras and projected out through the other hand chakra.

7) It is important to concentrate properly on both the left and right hand chakras. Success depends upon this. To concentrate more on the projecting hand chakra and not to give the receiving

hand chakra sufficient concentration would tend to weaken and exhaust the healer.

8) If you feel slight pain or discomfort on your hand while energizing, flick your hand to throw away the absorbed diseased bioplasmic matter. When energizing, the hand should be flicked regularly to throw away the diseased bioplasmic matter.

9) Energizing should be continued until the treated part is sufficiently energized. The affected part has enough prana if you feel a *slight repulsion* coming from the treated area or if you feel a *gradual cessation* of the flow of prana from your palm to the treated area. The flow of prana may feel like a warm moving current or just plain subtle moving current. The feeling of slight repulsion or cessation of flow is due to the equalization of pranic energy levels between your hand and the treated area. For beginners, energizing with prana may take five to fifteen minutes for simple cases and about thirty minutes for more severe cases.

10) Cross-check whether the treated area is sufficiently energized by simply *rescanning* the inner aura of the treated part. If it is not, then energize further until the treated part has sufficient prana.

11) If the treated part is highly overenergized, apply distributive sweeping to prevent possible pranic congestion. This is done by sweeping the excess prana with your hand to the surrounding area. Cross-check the result by scanning. If the treated part is slightly overenergized by three inches, then just leave it as is.

12) Prana or ki may also be projected through the fingers or finger chakras rather than through the hand chakra. The prana coming out from the finger chakras is more intense. If the projected prana is too intense, the patient may feel pain and a boring or penetrating sensation that is quite unnecessary. It would be better to master energizing through the hand chakras before trying to energize through the finger chakras.

In energizing with prana, visualization is helpful but not necessary. Just relax and calmly concentrate on the hand chakras. The result will automatically follow. The technique is simple, easy, and quite effective. Try it and judge for yourself.

In drawing in prana, there are several possible positions: Reaching for the Sky Pose, Egyptian Pose, and Casual Pose. In the Reaching for the Sky Pose, if you intend to draw in pranic energy through the left hand chakra, raise your left arm and turn the palm upward as shown in figure 5 on page 116. The act of raising the arm upward is like that of unbending a water hose. There is a meridian or bioplasmic channel in the armpit area which is connected to the left and right hand chakras. The unbending of this meridian allows prana to flow with minimum resistance. The act of concentrating on the left hand chakra is like turning on the water pump. By concentrating on the left hand, the left hand chakra is activated and draws in a lot of prana since there was an intention or expectation to draw in rather than to project prana.

In the Egyptian Pose, if you intend to draw in pranic energy through your right hand chakra, bend the right elbow until it is almost parallel to the ground. The arm is moved slightly away from your body to make a small opening in your armpit area. This has the effect of unbending the meridians in the armpit area. The palm is turned upward. This conditions the mind to receive prana. (See figure 6 on page 116.)

In the Casual Pose, if you intend to draw in pranic energy through your left hand chakra, let your left arm hang loosely and casually. The arm is moved slightly away from the body to allow a small opening in the armpit area. The palm is in a casual position and is not raised upward. (See figure 6 on page 116.) The casual position requires more concentration for beginners since the upward position of the palm which conditions the mind to receive prana is not used.

I usually use the Egyptian Pose because it is more comfortable and does not look too strange. This reduces resistance from the

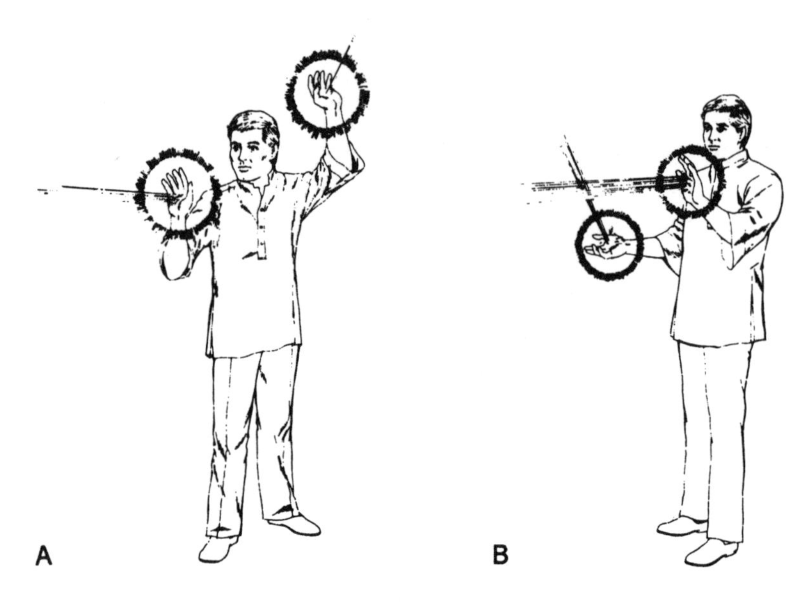

Figure 5. (A) Energizing with the Reaching for the Sky Pose; (B) energizing with the Egyptian Pose (standing position).

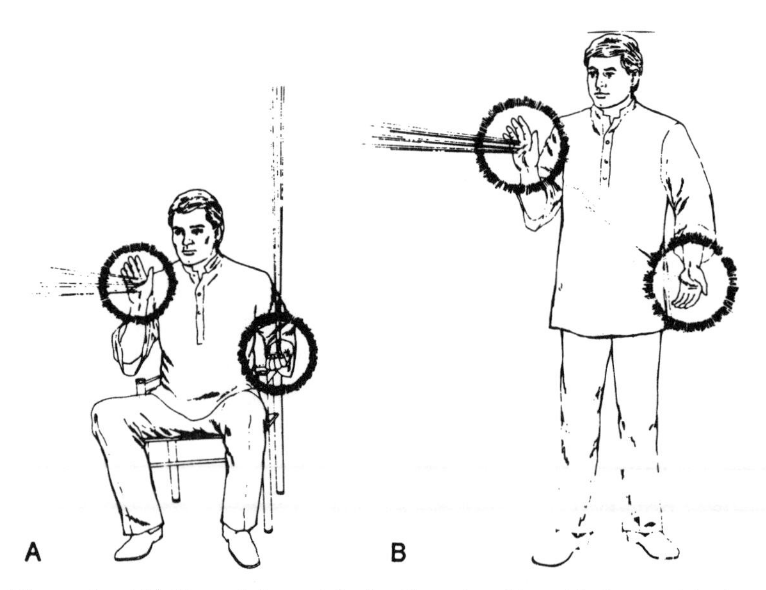

Figure 6. (A) Energizing with the Egyptian Pose (sitting position); (B) energizing with the Casual Pose.

patient. It is quite possible for a patient to partially and unintentionally block most of the prana projected to him by the healer if he finds the healer too strange or if he strongly rejects and disbelieves this form of healing. That is why it is better to establish rapport with the patient to make healing faster and easier.

STABILIZING THE PROJECTED PRANA

One of the potential problems in pranic healing is the instability of the projected prana. The projected prana tends to gradually leak out, causing possible regression or causing the illness to recur. This potential problem can be handled by thoroughly cleansing or sweeping the part to be treated and by stabilizing the projected prana. The projected prana can be stabilized in two ways:

- You should finish all energizing with prana by projecting blue prana. This is done by visualizing and projecting light-blue prana on the treated part.
- You can also just will or mentally instruct the projected prana to remain or stabilize.

You can perform this experiment to prove to yourself the validity of these principles and techniques. Use the following procedure:

1) Using the energizing-with-prana technique: project white prana on top of a table for about one minute and simultaneously visualize and form it into a ball without willing it to remain. This is the first pranic ball.

2) Project, visualize and form a blue pranic ball for about one minute without willing it to remain. This is the second pranic ball.

3) Project and form a white pranic ball for about one minute, and will or mentally instruct the pranic ball to remain for one hour. This is the third pranic ball. Make sure the locations of the

pranic balls are properly marked and that there are no strong winds that might blow the balls away.

4) Scan the three pranic balls to make sure that they are properly formed.

5) Wait for about twenty minutes and scan the three pranic balls again. You may find that the first pranic ball is already gone or greatly reduced in size while the second and third pranic balls are still quite intact.

Please, do try this experiment immediately. It is simple and easy to perform.

BIOPLASMIC WASTE DISPOSAL UNIT

The diseased bioplasmic matter has to be disposed properly in order to maintain a bioplasmically clean room and to avoid contaminating yourself and the other patients from this dirty bioplasmic matter. The diseased bioplasmic matter, when removed from the patient's body, is still connected to the patient by bioplasmic threads. The Hawaiian shamans (healers) or *kahunas* call the bioplasmic thread invisible *aka* thread. In esoteric parlance, this is called etheric thread. Unless the diseased bioplasmic matter is properly disposed, there is the possibility that it may go back to the patient.

To make a bioplasmic waste disposal unit, simply get a bowl of water and add salt into the water. It has been clairvoyantly observed that water is capable of absorbing dirty bioplasmic matter and that salt breaks down the dirty bioplasmic matter.

After sweeping or cleansing, you should flick your hands toward the bioplasmic waste disposal unit. You can perform this simple experiment: get two bowls of water, put salt in one bowl and do not put salt in the other bowl. Scan the two bowls before and after flicking the dirty bioplasmic matter to each bowl. The dirty bioplasmic matter can be obtained from sweeping your patients. Leave the bowls for about two hours and note the difference. You will notice that you could hardly feel the diseased bioplasmic matter in the one with salt, but can still feel it in the one without salt.

Some healers use water, sand, water with tobacco, meat and other organic matters as bioplasmic waste disposal units. Some American Indian shamans use twigs. The twigs are placed in the mouth of the shaman and the diseased bioplasmic matter is sucked out or extracted by the use of the mouth. The twigs are used to catch the diseased bioplasmic matter.

The diseased bioplasmic matter is clairvoyantly and symbolically seen by some clairvoyants as spiders or insects or other repulsive forms. Some shamans do not place anything in their mouths. They just simply suck out the diseased bioplasmic matter and "dry vomit" it out. For beginners, there is the danger of literally swallowing the diseased bioplasmic matter. Therefore, it is safer to use sweeping.

PRACTICE TIME

The following schedule should be practiced for at least twelve days. This is to prepare you in case there is a sudden need to heal somebody, such as your own child. This practice should enable you to heal simple cases like fever, loose bowel movements, gas pain, muscle pain, insect and bug bites, etc.

Sensitizing the hands: five to ten minutes per day;
Scanning: five to ten minutes per day;
General and localized sweeping: ten minutes per day;
Energizing with prana: ten minutes per day.

Preferably, these techniques should be applied on actual patients. If this is not possible, then get a friend or relative to practice on.

If you are one of those few who are not able to sensitize your hands on the first session, just proceed to sweeping and energizing with prana. Continue the practice of sensitizing your hands. You should be able to accomplish it in three to four sessions.

It is advisable to learn to heal simple cases first before going to more difficult cases. This is necessary in order to gain experience and confidence. It is preferable to heal at least thirty simple cases before trying to heal difficult or severe cases.

THREE THINGS TO AVOID IN PRANIC HEALING

1) Do not energize the eyes directly. They are very delicate and are easily overdosed with prana if directly energized. This may damage the eyes in the long run. The eyes can be energized through the back of the head or through the area between the eyebrows. There is a chakra (energy center) in each of these locations. It is safer to energize through the ajna chakra (the area between the eyebrows). If the eyes are already sufficiently energized, the excess prana would just flow to other parts of the body.

2) Do not directly and intensely energize the heart for a long time. It is quite sensitive and delicate. Too much prana and too intense energizing may cause severe pranic congestion of the heart. The heart can be energized through the back of the spine near the heart area. In energizing the heart through the back, prana flows not only to the heart but to other parts of the body. This reduces the possibility of pranic congestion on the heart. If the heart is energized through the front, the flow of prana is localized around the heart area, thereby increasing the possibility of pranic congestion.

3) Do not apply too intense and too much prana on infants, very young children (2 years old and younger), or very weak and old patients. With infants and very young children, their chakras (energy centers) are still small and not quite strong. Very weak and

very old patients have chakras that are also weak. Too much prana or too intense energizing has a choking effect on their chakras. This is similar to the choking reaction of a very thirsty person who drinks too much water in too short a time. The ability of very weak and old patients to assimilate prana is very slow. These types of patients should be energized gently and gradually. They should be allowed to rest and assimilate prana for about fifteen to twenty minutes before you attempt to energize them again.

If the solar plexus chakra (energy center) is suddenly over-energized, resulting in the choking effect on the chakra, the patient may suddenly become pale and may have difficulty breathing. *Should this happen, apply localized sweeping immediately on the solar plexus area. The patient will be relieved immediately.* This type of case is rare and is presented only to show the reader what to do in case something like this happens.

STEPS IN HEALING

1) Observe and interview the patient.

2) Scan the spine, the vital organs, the major chakras, and the affected parts.

3) Apply general sweeping.

4) Do localized sweeping in the affected areas.

5) Rescan the affected parts. In case of pranic congestion, scan to determine whether the congestion has been significantly reduced. For pranic depletion, scan to determine whether the inner aura of the affected part has become a little bigger or has partially normalized.

6) For simple cases, sweeping or cleansing is sometimes sufficient to heal the patient.

7) Energize the affected parts with prana.

8) Get feedback from your patient. If there is some pain left, ask for the exact spots and rescan those areas. Do more sweeping and energizing.

9) If the part is highly overenergized, do distributive sweeping to prevent possible pranic congestion.

10) Rescan the treated area to determine whether the affected area has been sufficiently decongested or energized. Thoroughness is the key to dramatic healing or very fast healing.

11) In pranic congestion, cleansing is emphasized. In pranic depletion, energizing is emphasized.

12) Stabilize the projected prana.

For beginners, it is better to scan before questioning the patient. This is to improve your accuracy in scanning. Scanning, like decision-making or other human faculties, can be influenced by suggestion. In scanning the patient, you should watch out for this possible flaw and try to recheck your findings.

For simple localized illnesses, general sweeping may be skipped. For infectious diseases, general sweeping should be applied even if it is just a simple eye infection or cold because the whole body is more or less affected. In infectious diseases, the outer aura usually has holes. The rate of healing is much faster when general sweeping is applied on these cases than when it is not.

CAN YOU HEAL WITHOUT SCANNING?

If your ability to scan is quite limited, you still can heal without scanning. For simple cases, just ask the patient what part hurts or is causing discomfort. Then apply localized sweeping and energizing. For some severe type of ailments, there are patterns that can be followed. For instance, patients suffering from heart ailments usually have imbalanced or malfunctioning heart and solar plexus chakras. Therefore, cleansing and energizing these two chakras would greatly improve the condition of the patient. The heart should be energized through the back heart chakra.

Although you can heal without scanning, you would be much more accurate and effective if you use scanning. Sometimes some of the malfunctioning chakras are located far away from the pains or ailing part.

WASHING HANDS

Both hands, up to the elbows, should be thoroughly washed with water or salt water before healing, after sweeping, and after energizing. This washes away some of the diseased bioplasmic matter left on the hands of the healer and also reduces the possibility of absorbing it into your system. Otherwise, this may manifest as pain in your fingers, hands, arms or your patient's symptoms may manifest in your body. Washing is also necessary to prevent *bioplasmic contamination* on your next patient. Your hands should preferably be washed with germicidal soap to reduce the possibility of infecting yourself (the healer) or the next patient.

CRITICAL FACTORS IN HEALING

1) The patient must be scanned and rescanned thoroughly and accurately. Correct bioplasmic diagnosis will lead to correct treatment. Proper rescanning will give correct feedback as to the effectiveness of the initial treatment.

2) The patient's bioplasmic body must be thoroughly cleansed to increase the rate of healing and to avoid radical reaction.

3) The patient must be sufficiently energized with prana. Insufficient energizing means slight improvement or slow rate of heal-

ing. Overenergizing on delicate organs must be avoided to prevent pranic congestion.

4) Stabilize the projected prana to prevent it from escaping or leaking out. Many new healers become overconfident and commit the serious mistake of not stabilizing the projected prana when their patients tell them how their condition has greatly improved. As a result, some patients experience recurrence of symptoms or ailments after about thirty minutes or after a few hours. Therefore, always stabilize the projected prana after energizing!

CLOTHING

Materials such as silk, rubber and leather tend to act as partial insulators to prana. Patients should be requested not to wear silk since it makes it difficult to project prana on them. Leather or rubber shoes and leather belts should preferably be removed to make general sweeping more effective. Some healers also remove their shoes when healing in order to absorb more ground prana.

DRAWING IN PRANA

When you began this study, you learned to draw in prana through one of the hand chakras. Now you will learn pranic breathing in order to absorb or draw in tremendous amounts of prana through the whole body from your surroundings. There are many types of yogic breathing that are used for different purposes. Yogic breathing that enables the practitioner to draw in a lot of prana and facilitates the projection of prana is called pranic breathing.

PRANIC BREATHING

When you do pranic breathing, it energizes you to such an extent that your auras temporarily expand by 100 percent or more. The inner aura expands to about eight inches or more, the health aura to about four feet or more, and the outer aura to about six feet or more. All of these can be verified through scanning. (See figure 7.)

Why not try this simple experiment: ask a friend to do pranic breathing for about five minutes. Scan your friend before he starts, and after he has done pranic breathing for about two minutes. Note the changes in the sizes of the auras. You may even feel a rhythmic pulsation or expansion. It is important that you perform this and other experiments so that your knowledge will be based on solid foundations.

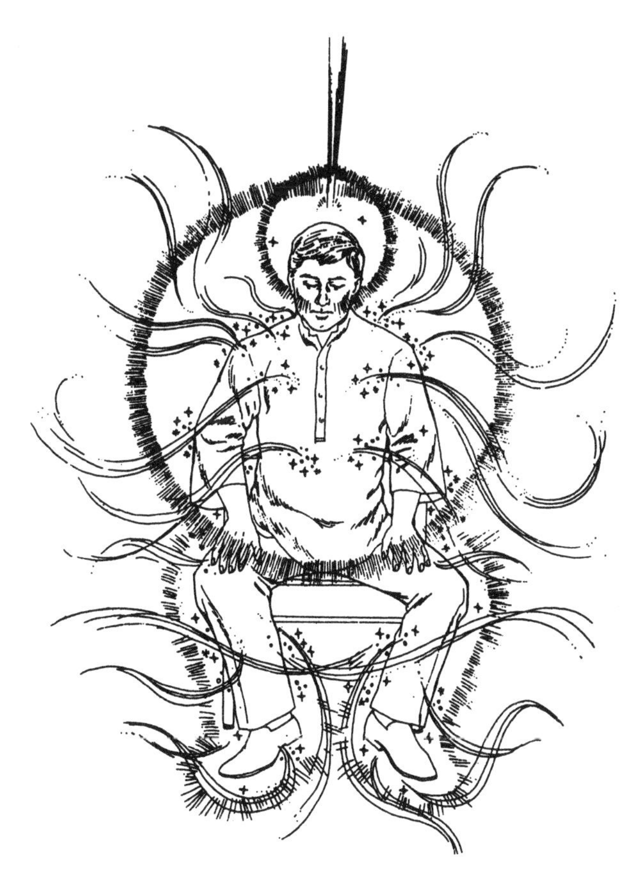

Figure 7. Pranic breathing. By doing pranic breathing you are able to absorb and project tremendous amounts of vital energy or prana.

METHOD 1: DEEP BREATHING WITH EMPTY RETENTION

1) Do abdominal breathing.

2) Inhale slowly and retain for one count.

3) Exhale slowly. Retain your breath for one count before inhaling. This is called empty retention.

METHOD 2: 7-1-7-1

1) Do abdominal breathing.

2) Inhale for seven counts and retain for one count.

3) Exhale for seven counts and retain for one count.

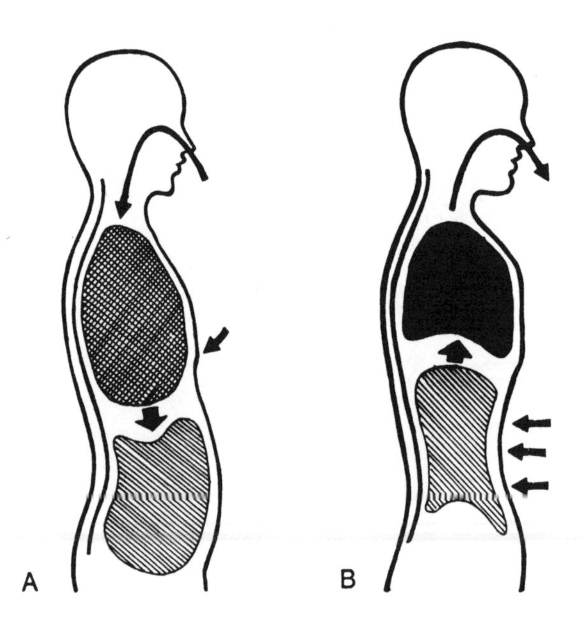

Figure 8. Abdominal breathing: (A) inhaling; (B) exhaling.

METHOD 3: 6-3-6-3

1) Do abdominal breathing.

2) Inhale for six counts and retain for three counts.

3) Exhale for six counts and retain for three counts.

Abdominal breathing expands your abdomen slightly when inhaling and contracts your abdomen slightly when exhaling. Do not over-expand or over-contract your abdomen. This would make breathing unnecessarily difficult. (See figure 8.)

The critical factors are the rhythm and the empty retention. Holding your breath after exhalation is called *empty retention;* and holding your breath after inhalation is called *full retention.* Through clairvoyant observation, it is noted that there is a tremendous amount of prana rushing into all parts of the body when inhalation is done after empty retention. This does not take place if the inhalation is not preceded by empty retention.

When drawing in prana, you may use either pranic breathing or the hand chakra technique or both simultaneously.

DRAWING IN GROUND, AIR AND TREE PRANA

There is a minor chakra in each foot. This chakra is called the sole chakra. By concentrating on the sole chakras and simultaneously doing pranic breathing, you can tremendously increase the amount of ground prana absorbed through the sole chakras. (See figure 9 on page 128.) Concentrating on the sole chakras activates them to a certain degree. Pranic breathing greatly facilitates or helps the sole chakras in drawing in ground prana. Drawing in ground prana is one way of energizing yourself. Ground prana seems to be more effective in healing the visible physical body than air prana. For example, wounds and fractured bones seem to heal faster with ground prana than air prana.

This technique of drawing in ground prana or earth ki is practiced in Chinese esoteric martial art, known as ki kung, the art of generating internal power.

1) Remove your shoes. Leather shoes and rubber shoes reduce the drawing in of prana by 30-50 percent.

2) Press the hollow portion of your feet with your thumbs to make concentration easier.

3) Concentrate on the soles of the feet and do pranic breathing simultaneously. Do this for about ten cycles.

Figure 9. Drawing in ground prana.

You can use the same principle to draw in air prana or tree prana through the hand chakras to energize yourself. To draw in air prana through the hands, just concentrate on the hand chakras and simultaneously do pranic breathing. (See figure 10.) To draw in tree prana through the hand chakras, choose a big healthy tree and ask mentally or verbally the permission of the tree to draw in its excess prana. (See figure 11 on page 130.) Put your hands on the trunk of the tree or near it. Concentrate on the center of your palms and simultaneously do pranic breathing. Do this for ten cycles and thank the tree for the prana. Some of you may experience numbness or a tingling sensation throughout the body. Once esoteric principles and techniques are fully explained, they are usually very simple.

Figure 10. Drawing in air prana.

Figure 11. Drawing in tree prana.

After energizing yourself, it is advisable to circulate the prana throughout the body. Visualize yourself filled with light or prana and circulate the prana continuously from the back to the front several times, then from the front to the back several times also.

SENSITIZING THE HANDS THROUGH PRANIC BREATHING

By now, most of you should have more or less permanently sensitized your hands. However, sometimes you may experience moments when the hands seem unable to feel or scan. This can be immediately remedied by concentrating simultaneously on the center of your palms and on the tips of your fingers while doing pranic breathing for about three cycles. This will cause the hand chakras and finger chakras to be activated, energized and sensitized so that you can scan accurately with your palms and with your fingers.

SCANNING WITH THE FINGERS

After sensitizing your hands, scan your own palm with your two fingers. Move your fingers slowly and slightly back and forth to feel the inner aura of your palm. Try to feel the thickness of your palm with two of your fingers and try to feel the different layers of the inner aura. Also practice scanning your palm with one finger. Always concentrate on the tips of your fingers when scanning with your fingers. This will activate or further activate the mini finger chakras; thereby sensitizing the fingers.

When scanning with your palms and fingers, always concentrate at the center of your palms and at the tip of your fingers. This will cause the hand and finger chakras to remain activated or to become more activated, thereby making the palms and the fingers more sensitive.

Being able to scan with the palms is not sufficient. You must learn to scan with your fingers. This is required in locating or proper scanning of small trouble spots. It is difficult to scan properly for small trouble spots with the palm because it may only feel the healthier surrounding areas around the small troubled spot. The small trouble spots are sometimes camouflaged by the healthier parts.

For instance, a person with eye problems usually has pranic depletion in the eyes, while the inner aura of the surrounding areas may be normal. Since the palm is quite big and the inner aura of the eyes is about two inches in diameter, it is likely that the palms may feel only the healthy eyebrows and forehead without becoming aware of the small trouble spots. This could be avoided if the fingers were used in scanning. The spinal column should also be scanned by using one or two fingers in order to locate small trouble spots.

In scanning a patient, you do not have to scan the outer and health auras. You were taught how to scan these auras in order to prove to yourself the existence of these auras. What is important is scanning the inner aura of the patient. In scanning the inner aura, it is important to feel the general energy level or the general thickness of the inner aura of the patient. This general energy level will be used as a reference or standard for comparing the conditions of some of the major chakras and vital organs. The accuracy of scanning will be affected if that area is scanned for too long because the scanned area will become partially energized.

It is important that you should be able to feel the pressure when scanning in order to determine the thickness of the inner aura of the part being scanned. Some of you may feel pain in your hands or fingers when in contact with a diseased part. The inner aura has several layers. In scanning the inner aura, you may feel pressure at about five inches and denser or stronger pressure at another layer about two or three inches away from the skin. Sometimes the inner aura of a part may seem normal. But when scanned further within, the next layer will seem rather thin, which means that the part is depleted. In scanning the inner aura, it is important to scan not only its first layer but also its inner layers. An advanced yogi or an advanced practitioner of ki kung has an inner aura that is comparatively big and has many layers. Sometimes the inner aura is more than three feet in thickness.

Scanning is also very useful in determining whether an infant or a child has a hearing or eyesight problem.

In treating serious cases, the eleven major chakras, the relevant minor chakras, all the major and vital organs, and the spine should be scanned thoroughly. It is through proper scanning and correct understanding of the nature of the ailment that the correct treatment can be determined.

SWEEPING WITH PRANIC BREATHING

General and localized sweeping is more effective when used with pranic breathing since more bioplasmic matter and prana are harnessed to remove diseased bioplasmic matter. When doing pranic breathing, the healer becomes more powerful because the etheric body (or bioplasmic body) becomes brighter and denser.

Just follow the instructions given in the first level of study for applying general and localized sweeping, and simultaneously do pranic breathing. With this type of sweeping, the patient is cleansed and energized simultaneously to a substantial degree. This type of sweeping is quite effective and very often sufficient to heal simple ailments. Sweeping can be done several feet away from the patient and with fewer strokes. You do not have to bother what hand position to use.

You may visualize luminous white prana sweeping and washing the patient from the crown to the feet when doing downward sweeping. Visualize the health rays being straightened. You do not have to do upward sweeping unless the patient is quite sleepy or has weak legs. When doing the upward sweeping, you may visualize the ground prana going up from the sole chakras to the crown chakra. This should be done after the patient has been cleansed sufficiently with downward sweeping. Applying upward general sweeping before applying downward sweeping may result in transferring diseased bioplasmic matter to the head and brain areas. This may result in serious harm to the patient, so don't do it.

You may or may not visualize when you do sweeping. For some healers, sweeping is more effective when accompanied by visualization. What is important is the intention to clean and energize the patient's bioplasmic body.

In sweeping, special attention should be placed on the back bioplasmic channel or the governor meridian,[1] which interpene-

---

[1] Students should obtain a good acupuncture chart or a book on the subject so that you can become familiar with the meridans. The functional meridian is also known as the Triple Warmer.

trates the spine, and the front bioplasmic channel or functional meridian, which is opposite to the spine. Except for the spleen chakra, almost all the major chakras are located along these two channels or nadis. Cleansing or applying localized sweeping on these two channels would clean the major chakras located along these two meridians resulting in a much faster rate of healing. You must remember that all the major and vital organs are energized and controlled by the major chakras.

When applying localized sweeping, visualize the fingers and the hands penetrating into the diseased part and the grayish diseased matter being removed.

ENERGIZING WITH PRANIC BREATHING

Prana is drawn in by using pranic breathing and projected through one or both of the hand chakras. You can practice the following exercise to energize yourself and others.

1) Do pranic breathing slowly for about three to five cycles and simultaneously calm and still your mind.

2) Continue doing pranic breathing and simultaneously put your hand or hands near the part to be treated. Concentrate on the center of your palm or palms.

3) Will or direct the projected pranic energy to the affected chakra, then to the affected part. This is a critical factor, and in many cases would produce rapid relief since the affected part or organ will be quickly provided with sufficient pranic energy. Your attention should be primarily focused on the hand chakra (or chakras) and on directing the pranic energy, and less on the breathing.

4) Stop energizing when you intuitively sense the patient has enough prana or vital energy. Rescan the patient to determine whether he or she is sufficiently energized. In level 1 (or elementary pranic healing), you were instructed to stop energizing when

you feel a slight repulsion or a cessation of the flow of energy. As you become more advanced in healing, this guideline is no longer valid because your pranic energy level becomes much higher compared to that of the patient. To equalize your pranic energy level with the affected part of the patient may result in pranic congestion on the part being treated.

5) If the patient has severe infection, burns, or cuts, then the treatment has to be repeated after half an hour or an hour. These cases consume pranic energy at a very fast rate; therefore, the treatments have to be repeated more frequently.

6) For pranic healers who are in the process of becoming proficient, relieving simple ailments may require five to seven breathing cycles and more serious ailments may require about twelve cycles or more. This is just to give you a rough idea. You may energize using your palm chakras or your finger chakras or both simultaneously.

Energizing should always be done simultaneously with pranic breathing. It is preferable to do pranic breathing for three to five cycles before you start energizing and to continue pranic breathing for two cycles after you have stopped energizing. This is to prevent possible general pranic depletion on the part of the healer.

DOUBLE ENERGIZING

There are two types of double energizing or energizing with two hands: parallel double energizing and non-parallel double energizing. See figures 12 and 13 on page 136. In parallel double energizing, simply place your hands facing and parallel to each other with the affected part in between them. In non-parallel double energizing, your hands are directed at the affected part but are not parallel to each other. In parallel double energizing, an intense energy field is created causing the hand to rhythmically expand and con-

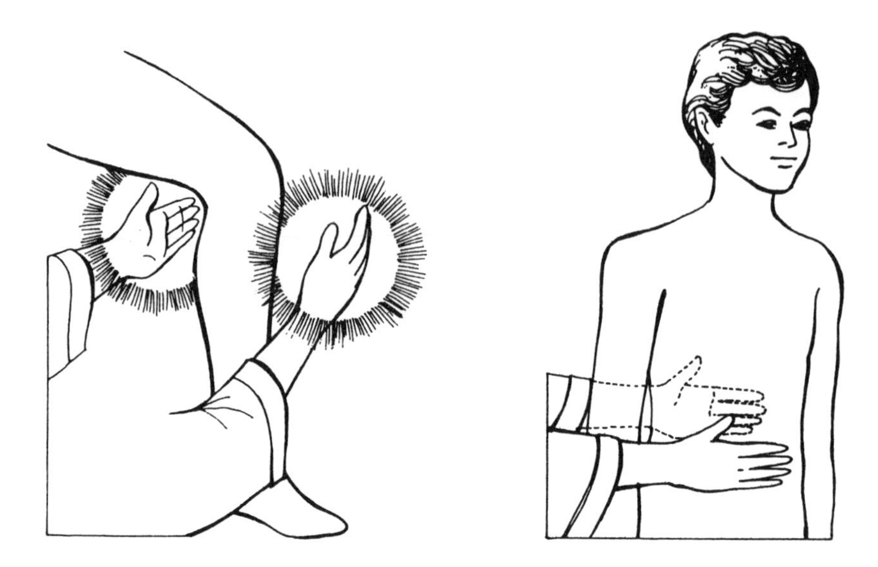

Figure 12. Parallel double energizing.

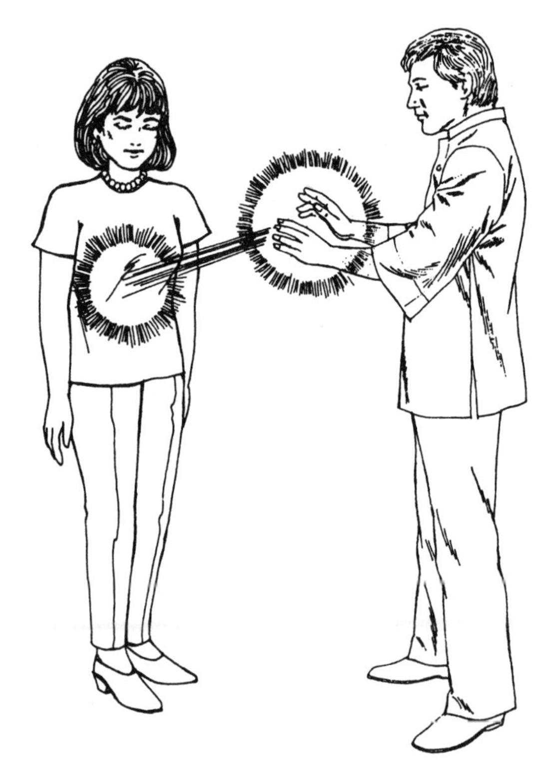

Figure 13. Non-parallel double energizing.

tract. A tingling sensation is felt, not only in the affected part, but also in other parts of the body. At times the patient may even feel a slight electric shock. Double energizing is usually used in cases that require a tremendous amount of prana. Cleansing must be done before double energizing. Double energizing can also be used to quickly relieve simple ailments or illnesses mentioned in level 1.

ENERGIZING: DISTRIBUTIVE SWEEPING TECHNIQUE

Energizing with the use of the distributive sweeping technique simply means the use of sweeping to redistribute excess prana from other parts of the body to the ailing part.

1) Clean the ailing part by applying localized sweeping.

2) Sweep the excess prana with your hand from the surrounding parts and chakras to the treated part.

This type of energizing is quite effective in healing simple ailments. But is not so effective in more serious cases since these types of ailments require a tremendous amount of prana.

DISPOSING DISEASED BIOPLASMIC MATTER

There are times when it is inconvenient or not possible to throw the diseased bioplasmic matter into a bioplasmic waste disposal unit. Should this happen, just simply visualize a fire beside you and throw the diseased bioplasmic matter into the fire. Then extinguish the visualized fire after treating your patient. You can also will the diseased bioplasmic matter to disintegrate when you flick it away. These two techniques are to be used only by more advanced healers.

For beginners, you can try to heal in open spaces and throw the diseased bioplasmic matter into the ground. It is a common practice among shamans to dispose of objects filled with diseased bioplasmic matter by burning them, exposing them in the air for prolonged periods of time or burying them underground.

UTILIZING GROUND PRANA IN HEALING

There is a greater concentration of prana just above the ground than in the air. The density of prana just above the ground is about four or five times greater than the prana contained in the air. This concentration of ground prana can be used for healing.

Ask your patient to lie down on the ground. A cotton blanket or a mat made of natural material may be used to lie on. Avoid using leather, rubber, synthetic foam, a synthetic mat or blanket, for they tend to act as insulators, which hinder the free flow of ground prana into the body.

Apply general sweeping and localized sweeping several times. Let the patient rest and gradually absorb the ground prana. The act of cleansing causes a sort of partial "pranic vacuum" that results in the rushing of ground prana into the bioplasmic body of the patient and into the treated part. Energy tends to flow from greater intensity to lower intensity or from greater concentration to lower concentration. Once the patient is cleansed, energizing from ground prana occurs automatically and gradually. The healer should preferably energize the patient after sweeping to shorten the time required to substantially energize the affected part.

This is also the reason why some shaman healers go to the extent of burying the patient in the ground so that he or she can absorb more ground prana. If one is not feeling too well, one can take a swim in the sea for ten to fifteen minutes to cleanse the bioplasmic body and after that bury his or her body in the sand to gradually absorb ground prana.

PRACTICE SCHEDULE

Follow the schedule below for about two weeks. You should also try to treat many difficult cases. If you follow the instructions in this book consistently, your healing skill will develop very rapidly. You will be able to do a lot of things that may be considered by others as impossible or miraculous!

1) Scanning with two fingers–five minutes.

2) Pranic breathing and drawing in of air prana through the hand chakras–five minutes.

3) General sweeping at a distance of three feet from the patient–five minutes.

4) Energizing with pranic breathing–five minutes.

APPENDIX B

Meditation on Twin Hearts

THE ILLUMINATION TECHNIQUE, or Meditation on the Twin Hearts, is a technique to achieve Buddhic consciousness or cosmic consciousness or illumination. It is also a form of service to the world because the world is harmonized to a certain degree by blessing the entire earth with loving kindness.[1]

Meditation on the Twin Hearts is based on the principle that some of the major chakras are entry points or gateways to certain levels or horizons of consciousness. To achieve illumination or Buddhic consciousness, it is necessary to fully activate the crown chakra. The crown chakra, when fully activated, becomes like a cup. To be more exact, the twelve inner petals open and turn upward like a cup to receive spiritual energies which are distributed to other parts of the body. The crowns worn by kings and queens are but poor physical replicas or symbols of the indescribably resplendent crown chakra of a fully-developed person. The fully activated crown chakra is symbolized as the Holy Grail.

The crown chakra can only be fully activated when the heart chakra is first fully activated. The heart chakra is a replica of the crown chakra. When you look at the heart chakra, it looks like the inner chakra of the crown chakra, which has twelve golden

[1] If you want to learn to practice meditation on the twin hearts, please visit the Mei Ling Healing Centers, listed in the Resources section at the back of this book.

petals. The heart chakra is the lower correspondence of the crown chakra. The crown chakra is the center of illumination and divine love or oneness with all. To explain what is divine love and illumination to an ordinary person is just like trying to explain what color is to a blind man. The heart chakra is the center of higher emotions. It is the center for compassion, joy, affection, consideration, mercy and other refined emotions. Without developing higher refined emotions, how can one possibly experience divine love?

There are many ways of activating the heart and crown chakras. You can use physical movements, hatha yoga, yogic breathing techniques, mantras or words of power, and visualization techniques. All of these techniques are effective but are not fast enough. One of the most effective and fastest ways to activate these chakras is to do meditation on loving-kindness or to bless the whole earth with loving-kindness. By using the heart chakra and the crown chakra in blessing the earth with loving-kindness, they become channels for spiritual energies; thereby becoming activated in the process. By blessing the earth with loving-kindness, you are doing a form of world service. And by blessing the earth with loving-kindness, you are in turn blessed many times. It is in blessing that you are blessed. It is in giving that you receive. That is the law!

A person with a fully activated crown chakra does not necessarily achieve illumination for he or she has yet to learn how to make use of the crown chakra to achieve illumination. It is just like having a sophisticated computer but not knowing how to operate it. Once the crown chakra has been fully activated, then you have to do meditation on the light, on the mantra *Aum,*[2] and on the gap between the two Aums. Intense concentration should be focused not only on the mantra Aum but especially on the gap between the two Aums. It is by fully and intensely con-

---

[2] *Aum* is a Sanskrit word for the Supreme Being; in Arabic, *Allah;* in Chinese, *Tao;* and in English, *God.*

centrating on the light and the gap between the two Aums that illumination, or samadhi, is achieved!

With most people, their other chakras are quite activated. The basic chakra, sex chakra, and solar plexus chakra are activated in practically all people. With these people, their instincts for self-survival, their sex drive and their tendency to react with their lower emotions are very active. With the pervasiveness of modern education and work that requires the use of the mental faculty, the ajna chakra and the throat chakra are developed in a lot of people. What is not developed in most people are the heart and crown chakras. Modern education, unfortunately, tends to over-emphasize the development of the throat chakra and the ajna chakra or the development of the concrete mind and the abstract mind. The development of the heart has been neglected. Because of this, you may encounter people who are quite intelligent but very abrasive. This type of person has not yet matured emotionally or the heart chakra is quite underdeveloped. Though he or she is intelligent and may be successful, human relationships are very poor, with hardly any friends and no family or a broken family. By using the meditation on the two hearts, a person becomes harmoniously balanced.

Whether the abstract and concrete mind will be used constructively or destructively depends upon the development of the heart. When the solar plexus chakra is overdeveloped and the heart chakra is underdeveloped, or when the lower emotions are active and the higher emotions are underdeveloped, then the mind would probably be used destructively. Without the development of the heart in most people, world peace will be an unattainable dream. This is why the development of the heart should be emphasized in the educational system.

People less than 18 years old should not practice the illumination technique since the body cannot yet withstand too much subtle energy. This may even manifest as physical paralysis in the long run. People with heart ailments should not practice Meditation on the Twin Hearts since it may result in severe pranic heart congestion. It is important that people who intend to practice

Meditation on the Twin Hearts regularly should also practice self-purification or character building through daily inner reflection. Meditation on the Twin Hearts not only activates the heart chakra and the crown chakra but also the other chakras. Because of this, both the positive and negative characteristics of the practitioner will be magnified or activated. This can easily be verified by the practitioner himself and through clairvoyant observation.

PROCEDURE

1) Cleansing the etheric body through physical exercise: Do physical exercise for about five minutes. Doing physical exercise has a cleansing and energizing effect on the etheric body. Light grayish matter or used-up prana is expelled from the etheric body when exercising. Physical exercises have to be done to minimize possible pranic congestion since this meditation generates a lot of subtle energies in the etheric body.

2) Invocation for divine blessing: Invoking the blessing of one's Spiritual Guides is very important. Each spiritual aspirant has spiritual guides, whether he or she is consciously aware of them or not. The invocation is required for one's protection, help and guidance. Without making the invocation, practicing any advanced meditational technique could be dangerous. You can make your own invocation. I usually use this invocation:

Father, I humbly invoke Thy divine blessing!
For protection, guidance, help and
illumination!
With thanks and in full faith!

3) Activating the heart chakra – blessing the entire earth with loving-kindness: Press your front heart chakra with your finger for a few seconds. This is to make concentration on the front heart chakra easier. Concentrate on the front heart chakra and bless the

earth with loving-kindness. You may improvise your own blessing with loving-kindness. I usually use this blessing:

Blessing the Earth with Loving-Kindness

From the Heart of God,
Let the entire earth be blessed with loving-kindness.
Let the entire earth be blessed with great joy, happiness and divine peace.
Let the entire earth be blessed with understanding, harmony, good will and will-to-good. So be it!

From the Heart of God,
Let the hearts of all sentient beings be filled with divine love and kindness.
Let the hearts of all sentient beings be filled with great joy, happiness and divine peace.
Let the hearts of all sentient beings be filled with understanding, harmony, good will and will-to-good. With thanks, so be it!

For beginners, this blessing is done only once or twice. Do not overdo this blessing at the start. Some may even feel a slight pranic congestion around the heart area. This is because your etheric body is not sufficiently clean. Apply localized sweeping to remove the congestion.

This blessing should not be done mechanically. You should feel and fully appreciate the implications in each phrase. You may also use visualization. When blessing the earth with loving kindness, visualize the aura of the earth as becoming dazzling pink. When blessing the earth with great joy, happiness and peace, visualize people with heavy difficult problems smiling–their hearts filled with joy, faith, hope and peace. Visualize their problems becoming lighter and their faces lightening up. When blessing the earth with harmony, good will and will-to-good, visualize people or nations on the verge of fighting or fighting each other reconciling. Visualize these people putting down their arms and embracing each other. Visualize them being filled with good intentions and filled with the will to carry out this good intention. This blessing can be directed to a nation or nations, a family or a person or a group of people. Do not direct this blessing on a specific infant or specific children because they might be overwhelmed by the intense energy generated by the meditation.

4) Activating the crown chakra–blessing the earth with loving-kindness: Press the crown with your finger for several seconds to facilitate concentration on the crown chakra and bless the entire earth with loving-kindness. When the crown chakra is fully opened, some of you will feel something blooming on top of the head and some will also feel something pressing on the crown. After the crown chakra has been activated, concentrate simultaneously on the crown chakra and the heart chakra, and bless the earth with loving-kindness several times. This will align the heart chakra and the crown chakra, thereby making the blessing much more potent.

5) To achieve illumination–meditation on the light, on the Aum and the gap between the two Aums: Visualize a grain of dazzling white light on the crown or at the center inside the head, and simultaneously mentally utter the mantra, Aum. Concentrate intensely on the point of light, on the Aum and on the gap between the two Aums. When mentally uttering the mantra Aum, you will notice that the Aums are not continuous and that there is a slight gap between two mantras or between two Aums. Do this meditation for five to ten minutes. When the spiritual aspirant can fully concentrate simultaneously on the point of light and on the gap between the two Aums, he or she will experience an "inner explosion of light." The entire being will be filled with light! He or she will have the first glimpse of illumination and the first experience of divine ecstasy! To experience Buddhic con-

sciousness or illumination is to experience and understand what Jesus meant when he said: "If thine eye be single, thy whole body shall be full of light" (Luke 11:34). "For behold, the kingdom of heaven is within you" (Luke 17:21).

For some people, it may take years before they experience an initial glimpse of illumination or Buddhic consciousness. Others may take months while others may take weeks. For the very few, they achieve initial expansion of consciousness on the first try. This is usually done with the help from an elder or a facilitator.

When doing this meditation, the aspirant should be neutral. He or she should not be obsessed with results or filled with too many expectations. Otherwise, he or she will be actually meditating on the expectations or the expected results rather than on the point of light, the Aum and the gap between the two Aums.

6) Releasing excess energy: After the end of the meditation, the excess energy should be released by blessing the earth with Light, Love and Peace. Otherwise, the etheric body will become congested and the visible body will deteriorate in the long run because of too much energy. Other esoteric schools release the excess energy by visualizing the chakras projecting out the excess energy and the chakras becoming smaller and dimmer, but this approach does not put the excess energy into constructive use.

7) Giving thanks: After the end of the meditation, always give thanks to your spiritual guides for the divine blessing.

8) Strengthening the visible physical body through massage and more physical exercises: After the end of the meditation, massage your body and do physical exercise for about five minutes. The purpose is to further cleanse and strengthen the visible body since more used-up prana is expelled out of the body. This facilitates the assimilation of the pranic and spiritual energies, thereby enhancing the beauty and health of the practitioner. Massaging and exercising after this meditation also reduces the possibility of pranic congestion or energy getting in certain parts of the body which may lead to illness. You can also gradually cure yourself of

some ailments by doing exercises after doing the Meditation on the Twin Hearts. It is very important to exercise after the meditation; otherwise, the visible physical body will inevitably be weakened. Although the etheric body will become very bright and strong, the visible physical body will become weak because it will not be able to withstand the leftover energy generated by the meditation in the long run. You have to experience it yourself to fully appreciate what I am saying.

Some of you have the tendency not to do physical exercises after this meditation but to continue savouring the blissful state. This tendency should be overcome, otherwise your physical health will deteriorate in the long run.

Sometimes when a spiritual aspirant meditates, he or she may experience unusual physical movements for a limited period of time. This is quite normal since the etheric channels are being cleansed.

The instructions may seem quite long but the meditation is short, simple and very effective! It requires only ten to fifteen minutes excluding the time required for the physical exercises.

There are many degrees of illumination. The art of "intuiting" or "direct synthetic knowing" requires constant practice (meditation) for a long duration of time. To be more exact, it requires many incarnations to develop facility in the use of this Buddhic faculty.

Blessing the earth with loving-kindness can be done in group as a form of world service. When done in a group for this purpose, first bless the earth with loving-kindness through the heart chakra, then through the crown chakra, then through both the crown chakra and the heart chakra. Release the excess energy after the end of the meditation. The other parts of the meditation are omitted. The blessing can be directed, not only to the entire earth, but also to a specific nation or group of nations. The potency of the blessing is increased many times when done in a group. For example, when the blessing is done by a group of seven, the effect or potency is equal to more than one hundred people doing it separately.

Just as pranic healing can miraculously cure simple and severe ailments, the Meditation on Twin Hearts, when practiced by a large number of people, can also miraculously heal the entire earth. This message is directed to readers with sufficient maturity and the will-to-good.

MEDITATION ON THE TWIN HEARTS

1) Clean the etheric body; do physical exercise for about five minutes.

2) Invoke for divine blessing.

3) Activate the heart chakra, concentrate on it, and bless the entire earth with loving-kindness.

4) Activate the crown chakra, concentrate on it, and bless the entire earth with loving-kindness. Then bless the earth with loving-kindness simultaneously through the crown chakra and the heart chakra.

5) To achieve illumination, concentrate on the point of light, on the Aum, and on the gap between the two Aums.

6) To release excess energy, bless the earth with light, love and peace.

7) Give thanks.

8) To strengthen the visible physical body; massage face and body, and do physical exercise for about five minutes.

Meditation on the Twin Hearts is a very powerful tool in bringing about world peace; therefore, this meditational technique should be disseminated. Permission is granted to all interested persons to reprint, recopy, and reproduce the Meditation on the Twin Hearts with proper acknowledgment to both author and publisher.

APPENDIX C

Meditation on the White Light

THIS METHOD of general cleansing and energizing is usually called meditation on the white light or meditation on the middle pillar. The middle pillar technique has been used by various oriental and occidental esoteric schools. This technique is divided into parts. The first part deals with general cleansing and energizing. The second part deals with the circulation of prana.

GENERAL CLEANSING AND ENERGIZING

1) Do pranic breathing and simultaneously visualize a ball of intense bright light above the crown.

2) Visualize a stream of light coming down from the ball to the crown, then gradually down to the feet. Visualize the white light cleansing and energizing all the major chakras, all the important organs, the spine, and the bones in the body.

3) Visualize the white light coming out of the feet and flushing out all the grayish diseased matter. Repeat the process three times.

4) Visualize a brilliant ball of light at the bottom of the feet. Draw in earth prana in the form of a stream of light from this brilliant ball of light. Inhale and draw in the prana through the

sole chakras up to the head. Exhale and let the prana sprinkle out of the crown chakra. Repeat this three times.

CIRCULATING PRANA

1) Visualize prana circulating from the bottom of the feet, up to the back of the body, up the the head, down to the face, to the front of the body, then to the feet. Circulate prana from back to front three times.

2) Reverse the circulation and circulate prana from front to back. Circulate three times.

3) Circulate prana from left to right three times and from right to left three times. The purpose of circulating prana is to evenly distribute prana throughout the body and to prevent pranic congestion in certain parts of the body.

This meditation can be used daily to improve and maintain your health. It is also used by some esoteric students before engaging in activities that require a lot of prana. You may perform this meditation before healing a large number of people. Once you become proficient in this meditation, you will literally feel your body tingle and will feel a strong current moving within and outside your body.

You may also use the excess prana generated to produce "synthetic ki" or navel ki by concentrating on the navel chakra for about ten minutes. Store the "synthetic ki" in the two secondary navel chakras located two inches below the navel. This is done by simply concentrating on two inches below the navel for about three to five minutes. Pranic breathing should be done simultaneously with the preceding instructions. Each of the secondary navel chakras has a big flexible meridian that is used for storing navel ki. In short, the two secondary navel chakras are warehouses for the "synthetic ki." The two secondary navel chakras are called *ki hai,* which means "ocean of ki" because these minor chakras are filled with "synthetic ki." It must be repeated that "synthetic ki" or navel ki is different from prana. The "synthetic ki" is synthesized by the navel chakra and may appear as milky white, whitish red, golden yellow, and other colors. The "synthetic ki" varies in size and in density. Ordinary people have very little "synthetic ki" compared to spiritual aspirants and practitioners of ki kung.

It would be advisable for you to learn to meditate on the white light and practice it every day. It makes your bioplasmic body cleaner, brighter, and denser, thereby making you a better healer.

Suggested Reading

Bailey, Alice. *Esoteric Healing*. Albany, NY: Lucis Publishing.

Bardon, Franz. *Initiation into Hermetics*. Wuppertal, Germany: Dieter Ruggerberg. (Available in the United States from Samuel Weiser. Write for information.)

Choa Kok Sui. *Pranic Healing*. York Beach, ME: Samuel Weiser.

Leadbeater, C. W. *The Hidden Side of Things*. Wheaton, IL: Theosophical Publishing House.

——. *The Inner Life*. Wheaton, IL: Theosophical Publishing House.

Powell, Arthur E. *The Astral Body*. Wheaton, IL: Quest Books, Theosophical Publishing House.

——. *The Causal Body and the Ego*. Wheaton, IL: Quest Books, Theosophical Publishing House.

——. *The Etheric Body*. Wheaton IL: Quest Books, Theosophical Publishing House.

——. *The Mental Body*. Wheaton, IL: Quest Books, Theosophical Publishing House.

Index

Pranic Healing Workshops

For people who are interested in attending Pranic Healing workshops, but are unable to travel to the Philippines, Dr. Choa Kok Sui and The Institute for Inner Studies recommend the following teacher for The United States of America:

Mr. Stephen Co
American Institute of Asian Studies
(Pranic Healing Workshops)
23555 Golden Springs Road, Ste. K1-2
Diamond Bar, CA 91765

Tel. No. (909) 860-5656
Fax No. (909) 860-7595

The Center for Pranic Healing, Inc.
20 East 49th Street
Suite 3A-C
New York, NY 10017

Tel. No. (212) 755-0197
Fax No. (212) 755-2578

Please feel free to write or call for more information about costs and times.